A POCKET GUIDE TO
ROCKS AND MINERALS

A POCKET GUIDE TO
ROCKS AND MINERALS

James Lagomarsino

Bath · New York · Singapore · Hong Kong · Cologne · Delhi · Melbourne

First published by Parragon in 2008

Parragon Books Ltd
Queen Street House
4 Queen Street
Bath, BA1 1HE

Produced by Focus Publishing
Designer Heather McMillan
Project Editor Guy Croton
Indexer Caroline Watson

See page 256 for photograph
copyright details
Text © Parragon Books Ltd 2008

ISBN 978-1-4075-1136-8
Printed in China

CONTENTS

INTRODUCTION 10

CARBONATES 44–59

ELEMENTS 60–71

HALIDES 72–77

OXIDES 78–89

PHOSPHATES 90–103

SULPHATES 104–117

SULPHIDES 118–129

SILICATES 130–201

ORGANICS 202–209

METAMORPHIC ROCKS
210–217

SEDIMENTARY ROCKS 218–237

IGNEOUS ROCKS 238–249

INTRODUCTION

Ever since the Earth's crust first began cooling from a molten mass into a solid form, rocks have been a feature of the terrestrial landscape. Over geologic time, tectonic movements have moved them around in a never-ending series of thrusts and shudders. They have been folded down into the depths as well as heaved into the air as huge mountain ranges. Nothing is forever though, and the combined force of the elements has ensured that eventually such physical structures are once again broken down into small fragments. These then begin a new journey toward being recombined into new rocks. This endless cycle is currently some 4.5 billion years old, and the manifold combinations of chemical and physical processes have created many thousands of different rock and mineral forms.

The study of these naturally occurring materials can be a fascinating experience that can be undertaken by any person, regardless of age or ability. Rock and mineral collecting is a wonderful activity for everybody, and one which grows with the individual person. It is also a pastime that need not cost very much to get involved in—after all, we are surrounded at all times by rocks of one form or another.

Opposite: Molten lava flows produce dramatic landscapes.

Is it a Rock or a Mineral?

There are strict rules about exactly what constitutes a rock and what makes up a mineral. These are that the substance must occur naturally, it must be a solid, it must have a regimented atomic structure, it must be non-organic, and its chemical composition must be consistent within certain limits. Rocks are basically all the solid, naturally occurring, materials that do not comply with the structural and compositional criteria for minerals. They do, however, include several substances that are derived from living things; examples of such non-minerals include peat, coal, jet, and amber. Most rocks are composed of a wide variety of mineral crystals.

Smithsonite is primarily composed of Zinc Carbonate.

The long, slow process of geological evolution throws up some fascinating rock formations.

Composition

Rocks and minerals are composed of a wide variety of chemical constituents, with some, such as silicon and oxygen, being the dominant elements. As a consequence of this, the silicates (chemical compounds of oxygen and silicon) are by far the most common, and make up more than 90 percent of the Earth's crust. Aside from these, a further six elements—aluminium, iron, magnesium, calcium, potassium, and sodium—are also common. Together with the silicates, they make up the vast majority of all the Earth's rocks and minerals. They are classified in a number of classes including the carbonates, oxides, phosphates, sulphates, sulphides, and native elements (such as silver and gold). These combine in various ways to make up the three classes of rocks— the igneous, the metamorphic, and the sedimentary. Besides these, there are also organic materials, such as peat, coal, amber, and so on. There are well over 2,000 different mineral types in all, and several thousand different kinds of rocks.

Characteristics of Rocks and Minerals

When faced with an unknown specimen, it can be a challenge to identify and classify it without recourse to the assistance of an expert. Fortunately, there are a number of specific characteristics that can be of great help in procuring a satisfactory identification. These include relatively simple ones such as color, hardness, and density, as well as much more complicated factors like triboluminescence and a specimen's particular radioactive properties. A large number of rocks and minerals can be identified by noting down a few of their basic characteristics and then comparing them with those on a suitable reference chart. Such information can be found in most books aimed at mineral collectors, as well as on countless websites. The properties used in this book—color, hardness, cleavage, fracture, crystals, specific gravity, luster, streak, and occurrence—are discussed in detail below.

Quartz and Pyrite.

Color

Although it is a good idea to start with a specimen's color when trying to reach a positive identification, it is important in most cases to remember to use it only as a guide, rather than as an immutable property. This is because the color of geological materials can vary tremendously, simply because of the presence of tiny quantities of foreign substances. These can be from all manner of sources, from bacterial to metallic, and are usually referred to as "trace impurities." Quartz is a good example of a mineral that can be transformed in this way—optically clear forms are free of such colorants, and are known as "rock crystals." When it contains certain iron and aluminium components, however, it can take on a violet or purple coloration, in which case it is referred to as amethyst. When there are

Above: Amethyst.

Right: Rose Quartz.

Peridot.

impurities composed of blends of iron, manganese, and/or titanium, the color changes to a vivid pink, in which case it is called rose quartz.

There are no hard and fast rules about which elements cause which colors, but as a generalization, one can say that iron usually produces brown, yellow, or red hues, whereas copper may turn rocks and minerals a blue or green color. Both of these can, however, also be responsible for black colorations, so it is advisable to be wary of using color to make an identification without some other supporting evidence. This is especially true where there is the slightest chance that the specimen concerned may have been artificially treated to alter its colors. Much of what is labelled "citrine" in the marketplace these days, for instance, is actually heat-treated amethyst, and most agates have been pressure treated to introduce vividly colored dyes.

Hardness

Rocks and minerals have varying degrees of hardness, and finding out the value for an unknown specimen is an important part of the identification process. Fortunately, there is a simple diagnostic table known as the Mohs Hardness Scale. This ranges from 1 to 10, with a specific mineral to represent each of the ten points—the softest being talc with a value of 1, and the hardest being diamond at the top of the scale with a value of 10. The full chart is shown here:

Hardness Value	Representative Mineral	Absolute Hardness
1	Talc	1
2	Gypsum	2
3	Calcite	9
4	Fluorite	21
5	Apatite	48
6	Orthoclase	72
7	Quartz	100
8	Topaz	200
9	Corundum	400
10	Diamond	1,500

Quartz (seen here with tourmaline inclusions), has a value of 7 on the Mohs Hardness scale.

Absolute hardness is a proportional representation of the relative hardnesses of minerals. On the chart above, for example, it can be seen that diamond is 1,500 times harder than talc. A specimen can be tested simply by attempting to scratch it with any of the various members of the group on the above list. Before doing so, however, it is a good idea to find an unobtrusive place to perform the test so that a good crystal face is not damaged by careless scratching. If the piece in question could be scratched with fluorite, but not with calcite, then its hardness would be somewhere between 3 and 4. If it and fluorite were able to scratch each other, then the value would be 4. Test kits with a series of graded scratching implements are readily available from specialist suppliers to make this task easier. It is a good idea to memorize the hardness of a few readily accessible substances for impromptu field testing.

Cleavage

Cleavage is where a rock or mineral splits along a specific plane as the result of specific weaknesses in its crystal structure. The way it does so is an important characteristic for a number of reasons, not least because it helps with identification. It is especially important when gemstones are being prepared by a jeweler, though, when the emphasis is on finding the best planes at all times. Before any testing is performed, it should be remembered that fracture and cleavage are two different things. Cleavage is where a smooth and reproducible split can be achieved along a given crystal plane, over and over again, whereas fracture is simply breakage. The results of such tests are given in a series of terms—these are: perfect, imperfect, good, distinct, indistinct, poor, and none.

The manner in which a rock or mineral cleaves is inherently tied to its atomic structure, and will always be parallel to a possible crystal face. This is an unwavering fact, and so when a specimen is being identified, it is important to know what symmetry the candidate rock or mineral has so that the cleavage planes can be compared. If a match can be obtained, then the identification can proceed for further verification with other tests. If there is no match, however, then the wrong candidate was chosen, and a new one must be found.

Vivianite has perfect cleavage in one direction and a splintery fracture.

Fracture

The way a rock or mineral fractures is a useful characteristic that can be used as an aid to identification. It is simply a measure of the way that a material breaks, and there are a number of different terms used to describe the nature of the broken faces. These are conchoidal, sub-conchoidal, uneven, jagged, splintery, and earthy. Fracture is not the same as cleavage—while not all rocks and minerals have cleavage planes, they all fracture in some manner, and specific materials will always display a recognizable type of break. The table below presents a brief overview of the different types of fracture, with examples.

Conchoidal—the most common type of fracture. It is a smooth, hollow, and curved break. For example: Obsidian and Quartz.

Sub-conchoidal—as with conchoidal, but less pronounced. For example: Scapolite.

Uneven—this is where the break has an uneven break line. For example: Smithsonite and Fluorite.

Jagged—this is similar to uneven, but has distinctly sharp points in the break line. For example: Native Gold and Native Silver.

Splintery—this is where a fracture results in a fibrous or needle-like break. For example: Kyanite and Vivianite.

Earthy—this is the result of a fracture in a poorly consolidated material. For example: Limonite.

Opposite: The geometry of a specimen's crystals can be a useful aid to identification.

Crystals

A mineral can be composed of any one of the seven crystal lattice systems, and being able to determine which type it belongs to can be very helpful when going through the identification process. Although difficult cases can require the use of spectrographic analysis equipment, most specimens can be satisfactorily examined with a hand lens. The seven types are:

Isometric or Cubic: A geometric system where all the axes are equal in length and the angle between them is 90°, forming a cube.

Tetragonal: A geometric system based on a rectangular prism with a square base.

Hexagonal: A geometric system based on a prism with a hexagonal base.

Trigonal or Rhombohedral: A geometric system based on a diagonally-stretched cube.

Orthorhombic: A geometric system based on a rectangular prism with a rectangular base.

Monoclinic: A geometric system based on a rectangular prism with a parallelogram as base.

Triclinic: A geometric system in which all three axes are of different lengths, with none being perpendicular to each other.

Individual Crystal Types

Acicular—these crystals are long, thin needle-shaped structures.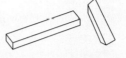

Bladed—these are long flat crystals.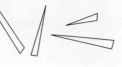

Blocky—these are box-like crystals.

Fibrous—these crystals are in the form of fibers, either individually or en-masse.

Platy—these crystals are flat and thin, being similar in shape to plates.

Prismatic—these common crystals are thin in comparison to their length, and have a uniform cross-section.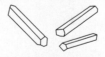

Pseudomorphs—these are crystals in which the original mineral's chemistry has been replaced by that of another, leaving the original shape intact.

Tabular—these crystals are shaped like rectangular tablets.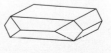

Aggregate Crystal Types

Arborescent and Dendritic—these two
types are very similar, with tree-like branches.

Botryoidal and Globular—these are
crystals that form in grape-like rounded masses.

Druse—these are outward-facing crystals that
usually form on the inside of hollow structures
such as geodes.

Encrusting—this is where a thin crust
of crystals forms over a parent rock.

Geode—this is where a hollow
stone is lined with crystals

Granular—these are crystals that have no clear
form, and are typically less than 1 mm across.

Lamellar—these are sheet-like crystals.

Massive—these are crystals that occur
in large, fine-grained accumulations.

Micaceous—these are crystals
that form in very thin flakes.

Nodular—these are crystals that have formed
as roughly spherical or circular systems.

Rosette—these are crystals which are
composed of petal-like structures.

Specific Gravity

The density of a specimen is a good indicator as to its overall chemical composition. It is expressed as a value called specific gravity—this is obtained by dividing its actual density by that of water. Since the weight of water is 1g per cm3, the specific gravity value for a specimen is simply a multiple of this figure, so, for example, a 1 cm3 piece of gypsum (specific gravity of 2.3) would weigh 2.3 g.

The chart below presents some representative values:

Specific Gravity	Weight Category	Example Minerals	Value
1–2	Very light	Borax	1.7
2–2.5	Light	Sulphur	2.0–2.1
		Gypsum	2.3+
2.5–3	Average	Quartz	2.65
		Calcite	~2.7
3–4	Above average	Fluorite	3.1
4–5	Heavy	Barite	4.5
		Molybdenite	4.7–4.8
		Marcasite	4.8
5–7	Very heavy	Pyrite	5.1
		Hematite	5.3
		Vanadinite	6.6+
		Cassiterite	6.6–7.0+
7–10	Extremely heavy	Galena	7.5+
		Native Copper	9.0
		Native Gold	19.3

Determining the specific gravity of a specimen is, in some cases, the best way to make a positive identification short of using complicated laboratory techniques. It is, however, still an unwieldy test to perform, and so the listing is generally best used as a rough guide to the relative weights one should expect when handling unidentified rocks.

Green garnet has a vitreous luster.

Luster

The way that the light reflects off a geological specimen is known as its "luster," and is a measure of its surface finish, as well as its transparency and refractive index. There are several terms used to describe the various types of luster displayed—a summation of these is presented here:

Type	Description	Example
Adamantine	– a very bright luster	Diamond
Vitreous	– looking like glass	Scapolite
Dull	– a non-reflective surface	Labradorite
Earthy	– looking like dried mud	Hematites
Greasy	– looking like grease	Vesuvianite
Metallic	– looking like shiny metal	Galena
Pearly	– looking like a pearl	Smithsonite
Resinous	– looking like tree resin	Mimetite
Silky	– looking like silk	Malachite
Sub-metallic	– looking like dull metal	Wolframite
Oily	– looking like the surface of oil	Peridot
Waxy	– looking like wax	Turquoise

Streak

When a geological specimen is rubbed against a suitable surface, it usually leaves a characteristically colored mark. This is known as its "streak," and is a very useful tool for identification purposes as it tends to be very consistent. In some cases it is a similar color to that of the specimen; however, in many others it is entirely different. A good example of where streak can be a good diagnostic tool is when trying to determine whether an unidentified mineral is composed of native bismuth or native arsenic. Both can look very similar, being heavy and black, but whereas the former has a silver to white streak, that of the latter is black. The test takes seconds to perform, and can easily be done in the field. It is not always this simple, though—many rocks and minerals, especially those that are transparent, produce a white streak. In such cases it may be that different tests have to be performed in order to distinguish between similar specimens.

Malachite has a light-green streak.

Purpose-made streak plates are available from specialist suppliers; however, an unglazed porcelain tile works just as well. It should be noted that these plates usually have a hardness of around 6.5—any specimens that have a hardness above this value will simply scratch the plate.

Occurrence and Localities

Although rocks and minerals surround the places where we live, unfortunately they are often rather dull, as the majority of domestic houses are built on stable sedimentary plains. In order to find the more interesting specimens, one has to either buy them from shops and on-line stores or venture out in the field to places where unusual geological events have taken place. Some of these are so rich in exotic species that they have become legendary amongst geologists and collectors. A few examples from around the world include those listed below:

The Arizona Copper Mines, USA

A major source of azurite, chrysocolla, cuprite, hemimorphite, malachite, turquoise, and wulfenite minerals, as well as many others.

Keeweenaw Peninsula, Michigan, USA

A major source of copper minerals.

Mexico

Many copper, gold, iron, lead, silver, tellurium, and zinc mines producing fine specimens.

Opposite and below: Unusual rock formations also often harbor rare geological deposits.

The multi-layered strata in these rocks demonstrate millions of years of development.

Minas Gerais, Brazil

One of the most famous sources of rare minerals in the world, as well as amethyst, citrine, rose quartz, rock crystal, smoky quartz, agate, and such gemstones as aquamarine, diamonds, tourmaline, and topaz.

Devon and Cornwall, England

A source of copper, iron, lead, silver, tin, and tungsten minerals, as well as many others.

Mount Vesuvius, near Naples, Italy

A range of rare volcanic minerals.

Harz Mountains and Saxony, Germany

A renowned region where more than 300 known minerals can be found.

The lead mines of Morocco

A major source of lead minerals such as cerussite and vanadinite, as well as other rare types.

Tsumeb, Otavi District, Namibia

A world famous source of over 300 zinc, lead, cobalt, and copper minerals.

Kimberly, South Africa

The most famous source of diamonds.

Kivu Mines, Democratic Republic of Congo

A major source of tantalum, tin, tungsten, and uranium minerals.

Kola Peninsula, Russia

A wide range of rare minerals.

Ural Mountains, Russia

A source of many valuable gemstones and rare mineral specimens.

Mogok, Myanmar

A major source of such gemstones as apatite, chrysoberyl, olivine, orthoclase, ruby, sapphire, spinel, topaz, and zircon, as well as many rare minerals.

Broken Hill, New South Wales, Australia

A world famous source of copper, lead, and silver minerals, as well as many others.

The crater of Mount Vesuvius in southern Italy is the home of many rare volcanic minerals.

Identification and the ID Key

When it comes to identifying specimens, the best way, without a doubt, is to have an expert tell you what you have before you. While this is all very well when you first start, you cannot always rely on having someone else around to do this. Besides, much of the fun involves doing the detective work yourself. These days, the task is easier than it has ever been—the internet is a fantastic resource, both for reference material and for access to experts who may actually be in far-flung parts of the world. There are many specialist societies that have huge amounts of on-line information about rocks and minerals, and some discussion boards are a veritable mine of knowledge. Digital cameras also keep both improving and coming down in price, so it is now possible to take high quality photos of your mystery items and then post images of them on web sites for others to assess. The quality of illustration in reference books has never been better, which makes identifying specimens much more straightforward. Before traveling to a new site, it is always worth buying the best geological maps of the area that you can find. If you are lucky, you may find that experts who are interested in the locality have produced some very detailed guides on the very place you are visiting. These often give lots of useful information about what you can expect to find and how to verify your finds.

A mixed stone like this is hard to identify.

While some specimens may need to be examined under spectral analysis or be put through a series of chemical tests for a positive identification to be made, many will succumb to some far simpler checks. These include recording the basic characteristics that have been listed above and then comparing them to property charts.

Property Chart

Name	Hardness	Cleavage	Specific Gravity	Lustre
Talc	1	Good	2.7.	Pearly to waxy
Limonite	1–5.5	Conchoidal	2.7–4.3	Earthy
Hematite	1–6	Irregular	4.8–5.3	Metallic or dull
Sulphur	2	Conchoidal to uneven	2.1	Vitreous to resinous or dull
Kaolinite	2	None	2.6	Earthy to dull
Gypsum	2	Poor to good	2.3+	Vitreous to pearly
Halite	2.5	Perfect	2.1+	Vitreous, waxy, dull
Muscovite Mica	2.5	Perfect	2.8	Vitreous to pearly
Calcite	3.0	Perfect	2.7	Vitreous, pearly, or waxy
Barite	3–3.5	Perfect	4.5	Vitreous, pearly, or dull
Hematite	5–6	None	5.3	Metallic or dull
Dolomite	3.5–4.0	Perfect	2.9	Vitreous, pearly, waxy
Sphalerite	3.5–4.0	Perfect	4	Resinous to adamantine
Siderite	3.5–4.0	Perfect	4	Vitreous, pearly, or waxy
Fluorite	4.0	Perfect	3.1	Vitreous to pearly
Apatite	5.0	Indistinct	3.1 - 3.2	Vitreous to greasy
Kyanite	5.0–6.5	Good	3.6+	Vitreous, pearly, or dull
Feldspar	5.5–6.5	Good	2.5–2.7	Vitreous or pearly
Garnet	6.5	None	~4.2	Resinous, vitreous, or dull
Olivine	6.5–7.0	Conchoidal	3.3–4.3	Vitreous
Quartz	7.0	Conchoidal	2.6	Vitreous to greasy
Tourmaline	7.0–7.5	Indistinct	3.0–3.2	Vitreous to resinous
Staurolite	7.0–7.5	Poor	3.7–3.8	Vitreous to resinous or dull
Topaz	8.0	Perfect	3.4–3.5+	Adamantine to vitreous
Corundum	9.0	None	4.0	Vitreous to dull
Diamond	10	Perfect	3.5	Adamantine to waxy

Rock and Mineral Collecting

Field Trips

Getting out in the field and collecting specimens is one of the most rewarding parts of studying rocks and minerals. If you are going to do this, however, there are various pieces of equipment that you will need, and some basic safety precautions to follow. No matter how keen you might be, there is no reason to compromise your own well-being, or that of those around you, for the sake of some simple precautions. These include wearing the proper clothing—if you are going anywhere even vaguely off the beaten track, you must make sure that all members of your party can stay warm and dry at all times. Further to this, dehydration and hunger can lead to accidents, so it is also vital to ensure that there is sufficient food and water to adequately sustain everyone. Cell phones can be a godsend in an emergency, but it is dangerous to rely on them—batteries can run out, or there may be no signal just when you need it most. If you are going off hiking on your own, make sure you write down exact details of where you are going, and when you expect to be back, and then make sure a responsible person has them. If there is no-one else around, lodge them with the local police station—but do make sure that you let them know that you have returned safely, or else rescue parties could be sent out unnecessarily.

If you are planning on going rock collecting, make sure that you are properly equipped and always tell someone where you are going.

Equipment for use in the Field

The equipment that you should carry for field trips includes the items listed here:

Safety Kit

Basic safety kit for when rocks are being struck with hammers and chisels—this includes eye protection in the form of goggles or safety glasses, sturdy gloves, and a hard hat. A small first aid kit does not take up much space, and so should always be part of your field equipment. It should include an eye bath in case someone gets hit in the face by small chips of rock.

Always wear protective gear when collecting.

Name	Symbol	Atomic number
Actinium	Ac	89
Aluminum	Al	13
Americium	Am	95
Antimony	Sb	51
Argon	Ar	18
Arsenic	As	33
Astatine	At	85
Barium	Ba	56
Berkelium	Bk	97
Beryllium	Be	4
Bismuth	Bi	83
Bohrium	Bh	107
Boron	B	5
Bromine	Br	35
Cadmium	Cd	48
Calcium	Ca	20
Californium	Cf	98
Carbon	C	6
Cerium	Ce	58
Cesium	Cs	55
Chlorine	Cl	17
Chromium	Cr	24
Cobalt	Co	27
Copper	Cu	29
Curium	Cm	96
Darmstadtium	Ds	110
Dubnium	Db	105
Dysprosium	Dy	66
Einsteinium	Es	99
Erbium	Er	68
Europium	Eu	63
Fermium	Fm	100
Fluorine	F	9
Francium	Fr	87
Gadolinium	Gd	64

Tools

This includes large and small hammers, large and small cold chisels and a bolster (wide chisel). You will also find it useful to be able to examine your specimens in detail, and so a high-powered magnifying lens is a useful addition to your equipment. Last, but not least, it is a good idea to make sure that you have some means of safely carrying your specimens home with you. Sturdy canvas packs are ideal, especially if you take plenty of bubble-wrap or newspaper to ensure that delicate samples do not get damaged.

Rock hammers.

Reference Material

You can never be too well informed. Geographical maps are a must if you are going anywhere remote, and geological maps will help you get the most out of your expeditions. Local guides can be a tremendous asset, and if you cannot find any, it is a good idea to check on the internet to see if there is any information about the locality. If you are going anywhere near the shoreline, tide tables can be a lifesaver—getting trapped on a narrow beach will not only endanger the lives of your party, but those of any rescuers as well. Similarly, always check the weather forecast before venturing out—a well planned trip is far more likely to be productive as well as safer.

A geological map of an area of coastline.

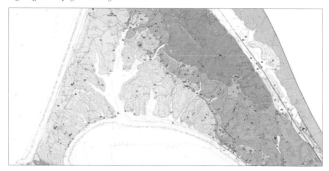

Record all your geological findings carefully.

Recording Equipment

Every field geologist should carry a notebook and pen to record the details of any specimens they find. In the short-term it may be possible to remember everything correctly, but as your collection grows it becomes more and more important to ensure that detailed information is available for every specimen. It is also a good idea to carry a small digital camera to record not only the specimens themselves, but also the details of the rocks that they came from. It can be a great help to be able to refer back to such images at a later date if the geology of the source needs confirmation.

Gallium	Ga	31
Germanium	Ge	32
Gold	Au	79
Hafnium	Hf	72
Hassium	Hs	108
Helium	He	2
Holmium	Ho	67
Hydrogen	H	1
Indium	In	49
Iodine	I	53
Iridium	Ir	77
Iron	Fe	26
Krypton	Kr	36
Lanthanum	La	57
Lawrencium	Lr	103
Lead	Pb	82
Lithium	Li	3
Lutetium	Lu	71
Magnesium	Mg	12
Manganese	Mn	25
Meitnerium	Mt	109
Mendelevium	Md	101
Mercury	Hg	80
Molybdenum	Mo	42
Neodymium	Nd	60
Neon	Ne	10
Neptunium	Np	93
Nickel	Ni	28
Niobium	Nb	41
Nitrogen	N	7
Nobelium	No	102
Osmium	Os	76
Oxygen	O	8
Palladium	Pd	46
Phosphorus	P	15
Platinum	Pt	78
Plutonium	Pu	94

Equipment for use at Home

The amount of equipment you amass at home will depend to a certain extent on how much room you have for such things. At the very least, you will need some cleaning utensils, such as brushes, scrapers, and various cleaning fluids. A low-power microscope can be a great help, but if this is not available, a stand-mounted magnifying glass and a strong lamp will allow you to examine your finds closely. A streak plate and a hardness testing kit will make the process of identification much easier, and, of course, it pays to acquire as many reference books as your budget and bookshelf space will permit.

A microscope is an essential piece of kit for the amateur rock and mineral collector.

A good magnifying glass is an asset at home as well.

Storing Specimens

The best way to store specimens is in proper display cabinets; however, few of us are able to afford such luxuries. In their place, almost any furniture unit with drawers can be adapted to fit the task. These should be equipped with lift-out trays, and each specimen should be placed in a box along with a data label. This should include the date and place of the find, the identification, if you have one, as well as any relevant geological information that you may have. It can be a great help to write a code number on the label, and then to glue a small tag with the same number on it on the specimen itself in an out of the way place to ensure that the label cannot be switched with another by mistake at a later date. It is also important to know which specimens must be kept out of the light. Vivianite, for instance, will quickly turn from an attractive blue-green color to a dull black if left exposed.

Polonium	Po	84
Potassium	K	19
Praseodymium	Pr	59
Promethium	Pm	61
Protactinium	Pa	91
Radium	Ra	88
Radon	Rn	86
Rhenium	Re	75
Rhodium	Rh	45
Rubidium	Rb	37
Ruthenium	Ru	44
Rutherfordium	Rf	104
Samarium	Sm	62
Scandium	Sc	21
Seaborgium	Sg	106
Selenium	Se	34
Silicon	Si	14
Silver	Ag	47
Sodium	Na	11
Strontium	Sr	38
Sulphur	S	16
Tantalum	Ta	73
Technetium	Tc	43
Tellurium	Te	52
Terbium	Tb	65
Thallium	Tl	81
Thorium	Th	90
Thulium	Tm	69
Tin	Sn	50
Titanium	Ti	22
Tungsten	W	74
Uranium	U	92
Vanadium	V	23
Xenon	Xe	54
Ytterbium	Yb	70
Yttrium	Y	39
Zinc	Zn	30
Zirconium	Zr	40

The Rock Cycle

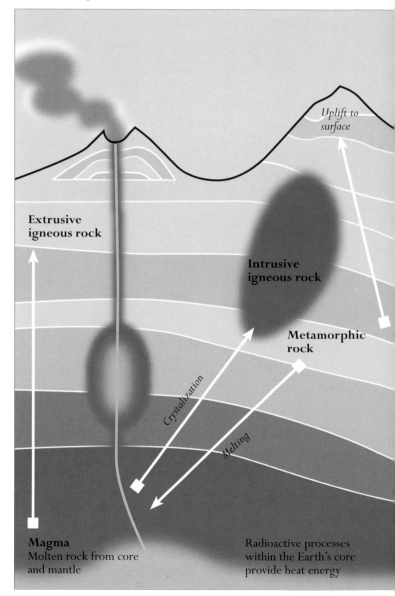

Uplift to surface

Extrusive igneous rock

Intrusive igneous rock

Metamorphic rock

Crystallization

Melting

Magma
Molten rock from core and mantle

Radioactive processes within the Earth's core provide heat energy

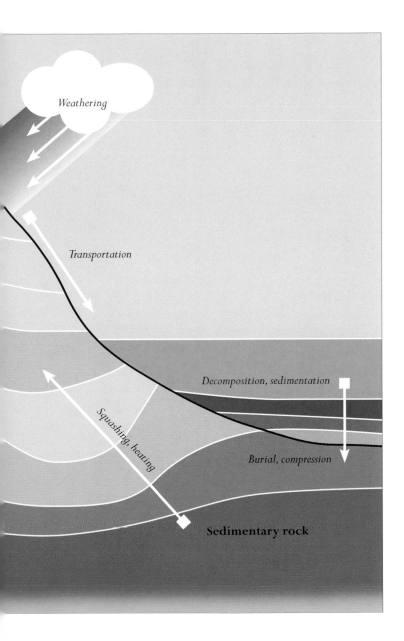

Weathering

Transportation

Decomposition, sedimentation

Squashing, heating

Burial, compression

Sedimentary rock

Geological Timelines

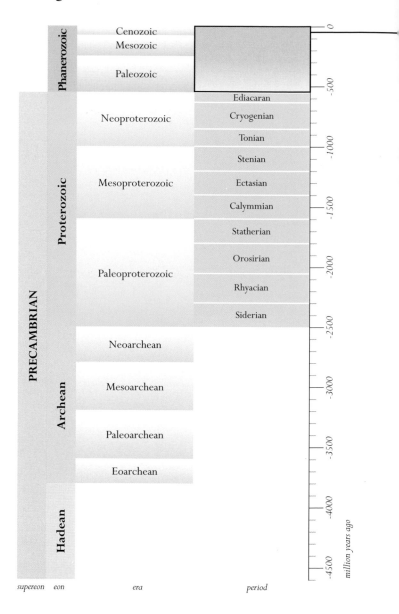

| supereon | eon | era | period | million years ago |

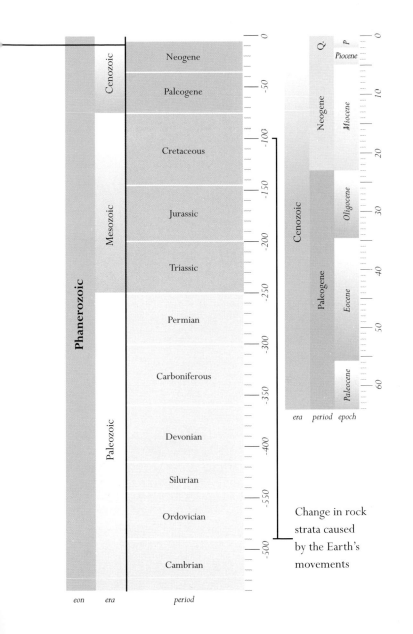

Neogene

Paleogene

Cretaceous

Jurassic

Triassic

Permian

Carboniferous

Devonian

Silurian

Ordovician

Cambrian

Cenozoic

Mesozoic

Paleozoic

Phanerozoic

0

-50

-100

-150

-200

-250

-300

-350

-400

-450

-500

-550

eon

era

period

Q.

P

Piocene

Neogene

Miocene

Oligocene

Paleogene

Eocene

Paleocene

Cenozoic

0

10

20

30

40

50

60

era period epoch

Change in rock strata caused by the Earth's movements

CARBONATES

The Carbonates are a large group of minerals that contain carbonate salts and form a major part of the Earth's crust. They have the general formula XCO_3^{2-}, in which X represents one or more metallic elements. Most share a similar chemistry, with this being reflected in the fact that they often have similar physical properties. A typical carbonate mineral is soft, transparent, has light or colorful colors, good cleavage, a white streak, and is of average or above average density.

Many of these minerals display threefold or "trigonal" crystal systems—this is due to the fact that the three oxygen atoms which make up the main part of the carbonate molecule lie equidistant from an inner carbon atom, creating a triangular structure. This symmetry is continued from atomic scale upward, something that is reflected in the resultant shape of the crystal.

There are three main groups of carbonates—these are the Calcite Group (examples include Siderite and Rhodochrosite), the Dolomite Group (including Dolomite and Ankerite), and the Aragonite Group (including Aragonite and Strontianite). The distinctions between each of these groups being made on a crystallographic basis.

MALACHITE

Copper(II) Carbonate Hydroxide Cu$_2$CO$_3$(OH)$_2$

Malachite is a soft green mineral which usually features swirling patterns of dark green bands. It is composed of a form of copper carbonate, and usually occurs where there are both copper and limestone deposits. It is often found in association with azurite, goethite, or calcite. The mineral's strong and persistent color when ground into a powder once made it a popular ingredient for making green paint. This was done from antiquity until about the year 1800; it was, for instance, extracted at King Solomon's Mines for over three thousand years. It has since been replaced by synthetic alternatives. Malachite remains a popular stone in the jewelry trade.

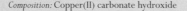

Composition: Copper(II) carbonate hydroxide

Color: Green

Hardness: 3.5–4

Cleavage: Perfect

Fracture: Conchoidal or shards

Crystals: Massive, botryoidal, or stalactitic

Specific Gravity: 3.6–4

Luster: Vitreous—Silky

Streak: Light green

Occurrence: Russia (Ural mountains) Democratic Republic of Congo, Namibia, Mexico, Australia, England, France, Israel, and the USA

AZURITE

Copper Carbonate $Cu_3(CO_3)_2(OH)_2$

Azurite, which can be found in a variety of structural forms, is a carbonate mineral that is popular with collectors, jewelers, and artists because of its vivid blue coloration. This comes from its high copper content. It has been used as a base ingredient for dyes and paints from the earliest days of civilization. It is frequently associated with malachite (as can be seen in the image here), and this can lead to rocks that are colored with strong bands of green and blue. It is not an important ore of copper, but good specimens are highly prized for display purposes.

Composition: Copper Carbonate

Color: Azure to pale blue

Hardness: 3.5–4

Cleavage: Good in one direction, moderate in another

Fracture: Conchoidal and brittle

Crystals: Transparent to opaque; monoclinic/variable

Specific Gravity: 3.7+

Luster: Vitreous to dull

Streak: Blue

Occurrence: Worldwide, especially USA, Mexico, Namibia, Congo, Morocco, Australia, and Europe

CALCITE *Calcium Carbonate CaCO₃*

Composition: Calcium Carbonate

Color: Variable

Hardness: 3

Crystals: Transparent to translucent; trigonal

Specific Gravity: ~2.7

Luster: Vitreous, pearly, or waxy

Streak: White

Occurrence: Worldwide

Calcite is a soft carbonate mineral that forms a significant part of the Earth's crust—consequently, many different kinds are found in a wide variety of geological environments. These include several parts of the United States, Mexico, and Brazil, as well as across large regions of Europe, Asia, and Africa. Fortunately, it is easy to determine when a specimen is formed from calcium carbonate, as it froths quickly on contact with acids—even with weak ones such as vinegar. Other similar carbonate minerals, such as Dolomite, do not effervesce nearly as readily.

Calcium Carbonate CaCO₃ RED CALCITE

Calcite is comprised of calcium carbonate—this factor alone is not enough to identify it though, as there are also two other major categories of minerals with the same chemical composition. These do have different crystal structures, however, with the most common of the two being Aragonite. This has an orthorhombic geometry, whereas Vaterite, which is much rarer, has a hexagonal system; calcite, on the other hand is trigonal. The example seen here is of a red-colored variety of this rock.

Composition: Calcium Carbonate

Color: Red to orange

Hardness: 3

Crystals: Transparent to translucent; trigonal

Specific Gravity: ~2.7

Luster: Vitreous to dull

Streak: White

Occurrence: Worldwide

BLUE CALCITE *Calcium Carbonate CaCO₃*

Composition: Calcium Carbonate

Hardness: 3

Fracture: Conchoidal

Crystals: Transparent to translucent; trigonal

Specific Gravity: ~2.7

Luster: Vitreous to dull

Streak: White

Occurrence: Worldwide

Calcite occurs in a spectacular array of colors and over 300 different crystal variants, all of which have perfect cleavage in three directions, forming rhombohedrons. They can range from being completely clear to white, orange, red, brown, yellow, blue, or green. The different colors are due to the presence of varying levels of chemical impurities, with the most common of these being the metallic elements cobalt, iron, manganese, magnesium, and zinc. The example seen here is of a blue colored variety.

Calcium Carbonate CaCO$_3$ ICELAND SPAR

I celand Spar is a transparent form of calcite that has
excellent cleavage faces—indeed, these can be so
well formed that good examples can look just like a
block of glass. The first significant source of specimens
was discovered in a mine in Eskifjord, Iceland, hence
the derivation of the name. These days it is also found
in other locations in Sweden, England, Austria, Russia,
Brazil, USA, and Australia. When light passes through
it, it produces a double refraction; as a result of this
property, it has been used to study the behavior of light,
as well as in specialist optical instruments. Individual
crystals can exceed 2 in (45 cm).

Hardness: 3

Fracture: Conchoidal

Crystals: Transparent; trigonal

Specific Gravity: Approx. 2.7

Luster: Vitreous to dull

Streak: White

Occurrence: Iceland, Sweden,
England, Austria, Russia,
Brazil, USA, Australia

SMITHSONITE

ZnCO₃ Zinc Carbonate

Smithsonite, which is a zinc carbonate mineral that is usually found in a botryoidal (grape-like) or globular form, is named after the founder of the Smithsonian Institute, James Smithson. It occurs in a wide variety of colors, from colorless to various hues of blue, green, purple, yellow, or white, and has an unusually waxy luster. It is commonly associated with other minerals such as cerussite, limonite, dolomite, calcite, and so on and is used as a minor ore of zinc. Its distinctive crystal structure, good cleavage, and characteristic fracture lines make it easy to distinguish from other similar minerals such as hemimorphite and prehnite.

Color: Very variable; green, blue, purple, yellow, white, colourless, and many others

Hardness: 4–4.5

Cleavage: Perfect in three directions forming rhombohedrons

Fracture: Uneven

Crystals: Transparent to translucent; trigonal

Specific Gravity: 4.4

Luster: Pearly to resinous or vitreous

Streak: White

Occurrence: Southern Africa, USA, Mexico, Greece, Poland, Belgium, and many others

ARAGONITE
Calcium Carbonate CaCO₃

Aragonite, which has the same chemical formula as calcite, is a common carbonate mineral that is found in many parts of the world. It has a crystal structure that often results in specimens with very interesting shapes and colors—this makes it very popular with collectors. It is named after Aragon in Spain, where it was first discovered, but other notable sources include Morocco, several places in Europe, as well as the south-western United States. It is typically formed where there are voids between rocks—especially those which are volcanic—and is commonly associated with a large number of other minerals such as gypsum, barite, dolomite, quartz, and so on.

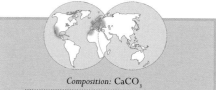

Composition: CaCO₃

Color: From colorless to red, brown, yellow, orange, green, or blue

Hardness: 3.5–4

Cleavage: In one direction (pinacoidal)

Fracture: Sub-conchoidal

Crystals: Extremely variable; orthorhombic

Specific Gravity: 2.9

Luster: Vitreous to dull

Streak: White

Occurrence: Many parts of Europe, Morocco, and south-western North America

CERUSSITE *Lead Carbonate PbCO₃*

Color: Typically colorless or white
—also gray, green, or yellow

Hardness: 3–3.75

Cleavage: Good in one direction

Fracture: Conchoidal and brittle

Crystals: Transparent to
translucent; orthorhombic

Specific Gravity: 6.5+

Occurrence: Australia, Congo,
Namibia, Germany, Morocco,
and USA (Arizona)

Cerussite, which used to be known as "lead-spar" or "white-lead-ore," is a carbonate mineral that is an important industrial source of lead. It forms colorless, white or gray crystals that vary from transparent to translucent, and are often twinned in a characteristic manner. These are brittle, and have smooth faces with an adamantine, sub-metallic, or greasy luster. Cerussite also occurs in massive or fibrous forms, and is often associated with galena deposits as well as barite, calcite, and anglesite. Identification is relatively straightforward, as no other mineral has pseudo-hexagonal twinned crystals with both conchoidal fracture and a high specific gravity. It has a white or colorless streak.

Lead Carbonate PbCO₃ WHITE CERUSSITE

White cerussite was used for many years as a primary pigment of white paint. Widespread recognition of its toxicity, however, resulted in it being withdrawn from the manufacturing process in relatively recent years. Despite it being a very delicate mineral that needs careful handling, specimens with well formed crystal structures are popular with mineral collectors—the best examples coming from the famous mines at Tsumeb, Namibia. Other sources include the Broken Hill mines in New South Wales, Australia, as well as Congo, Morocco, Germany, and several prominent sites in the United States. This mineral has an adamantine, sub-metallic, or greasy luster and a white streak.

Color: White

Hardness: 3–3.5

Cleavage: Good in one direction

Fracture: Conchoidal and brittle

Crystals: Orthorhombic and transparent

Specific Gravity: 6.5+

Occurrence: Namibia, Congo, Morocco, Australia, Germany, and USA

ELEMENTS

The elemental minerals are naturally occurring substances that are both relatively pure and have a clearly defined structure. They are well represented in the mineral record, with more than a hundred different types being found. These are generally referred to as "native" materials, and include metals such as gold, silver, and copper, as well as non-metallic substances such as sulphur. Most of the native metals are relatively pure (typically more than 95 percent), but usually have small quantities of other elements as impurities.

Most elemental minerals are very rare, with the exception of sulphur and graphite. The former has been collected since ancient times, when it was thought to have healing qualities. These days sulphur is an important industrial chemical, being used for all kinds of applications including the production of tires and for pesticides. Graphite, which is the most stable form of carbon, is a very soft, common crystalline substance that is formed by the metamorphosis of carbon-bearing materials, especially those of an organic origin, such as coal. It is another important commercial material, being used in the manufacture of industrial lubricants as well as in the cores of nuclear reactors. Diamond is also a crystalline form of carbon; however, it is not only very rare, but also the hardest naturally occurring substance.

NATIVE SILVER *Ag*

Color: Silver; black when weathered

Hardness: 2.5–3

Cleavage: None

Fracture: Jagged

Crystals: Isometric and opaque

Specific Gravity: 10–12, dependant on purity

Occurrence: Michigan and Arizona, USA, Cobalt, Ontario, Chile, and Germany

Silver sometimes occurs naturally in a native form—such specimens are rare, and usually composed of intertwined wires. The piece pictured here, however, is flattened and sheet-like. When it is freshly exposed, silver has a bright metallic luster, but once weathered it tarnishes to a matt black finish. It also has a silver-white streak. Silver is one of the first metals to have been extracted and worked by man and has been used in jewelry ever since. When photographic films were first invented, silver—which is very light-sensitive—was one of the primary ingredients. Consequently, there was a great demand for it and its value rose significantly. It is often associated with quartz, as well as with various minerals that contain copper, lead, cobalt, and arsenic.

Au NATIVE GOLD

G old is a very stable, un-reactive metallic element that occurs naturally in a pure form as nuggets, flakes, wires, and grains. Large pieces are, however, exceptionally rare, and it is more usually found as tiny flakes in river beds or as minuscule flecks on other mineral specimens. It is not only extremely desirable for its material value, but well formed nuggets are also highly sought after by collectors and are worth far more than their direct assay value. Gold's spectacular looks, along with the fact that it does not tarnish and is easy to work, has made it highly prized for the manufacture of religious and ceremonial artefacts as well as for personal adornments since human civilization began. It has a strong metallic luster and a golden yellow streak.

Color: Golden yellow to white

Hardness: 2.5–3

Cleavage: None

Fracture: Jagged

Crystals: Opaque, isometric/ nuggets or grains

Specific Gravity: 19.3

Occurrence: California and South Dakota, USA, Siberia, Russia, South Africa, Canada, and others

NATIVE COPPER
Cu

Copper occurs naturally in its native state in a variety of forms—these include large or "massive" pieces, thin wires, and extensive branch-like shapes. It can sometimes also be found in mines and quarries as precipitates where iron-bearing structures such as pipes are in contact with the ground. It used to be one of the main sources of copper; however, thousands of years of human extraction have more or less depleted it as an industrial source. Fine specimens are highly sought after by collectors though, especially if they display good crystal structures. Native copper usually has a dark tarnish, and has to be chemically cleaned to obtain the bright finish seen here.

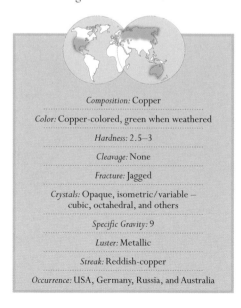

Composition: Copper

Color: Copper-colored, green when weathered

Hardness: 2.5–3

Cleavage: None

Fracture: Jagged

Crystals: Opaque, isometric/variable — cubic, octahedral, and others

Specific Gravity: 9

Luster: Metallic

Streak: Reddish-copper

Occurrence: USA, Germany, Russia, and Australia

NATIVE ARSENIC *As*

Color: Silvery-white when freshly exposed, dark gray to black when tarnished

Hardness: 3–4

Cleavage: Perfect in one direction

Fracture: Uneven

Crystals: Opaque; trigonal

Specific Gravity: 5.4–5.9+

Occurrence: China, Peru, SW England, France, Norway, Germany, Italy, Japan, USA

Arsenic is a highly toxic metallic element that tarnishes quickly when exposed to air. Although it does occur in its native form, this is rare, and it is far more commonly found as arsenide and arsenate minerals. The most prevalent of these is arsenopyrite (FeAsS), although others include realgar, and orpiment, both of which were, until recently, used as popular pigments for paints. Native arsenic is usually found in botryoidal forms in association with minerals such as cinnabar, silver, or barite, and has a garlic smell when rubbed. The specimen seen here, which was found in Saxony in eastern Germany, is composed of native arsenic on arsenopyrite.

Bi NATIVE BISMUTH

Bismuth is a heavy metallic element that has the symbol Bi—it has a silvery-gray color when freshly exposed, but this dulls to a sometimes iridescent tarnish with time. Although it does occur naturally in its native form, it is more commonly found in the ores bismuthinite and bismite—these are mined in large quantities in China, Peru, and Mexico. Native bismuth, which is usually associated with its own ores or those of cobalt and silver, is formed as the end product of the decay of uranium and thorium. It is used in the cosmetic and healthcare industries, as well as a safe substitute for lead in products such as solder and fishing weights.

Color: Silver-white; sometimes iridescent when tarnished

Hardness: 2–2.5

Cleavage: Perfect in one direction

Fracture: Uneven or jagged

Crystals: Opaque; trigonal

Specific Gravity: 9.7–9.8

Occurrence: USA, Australia, Bolivia, Germany, Devon in England

DIAMOND *Carbon C*

Color: Jewelry grades typically colorless; also yellow, blue, pink, green, black

Hardness: 10

Cleavage: Perfect in 4 directions forming octahedrons

Fracture: Conchoidal

Crystals: Transparent to translucent

Occurrence: South Africa, Russia, India, Brazil, Australia, Arkansas, USA, Africa

Diamond, which is a pure form of crystalline carbon, is the hardest known mineral, and defines the top of the Mohs hardness scale; this makes it easy to identify in the field. Optically clear specimens have always been highly prized, although these days synthetic equivalents are becoming more commonplace. It can occur in a number of different color forms, including those which have yellow, blue, pink, green, and black hues. It has perfect cleavage in four directions, which makes it ideal for use in jewelry. Diamond has an adamantine to waxy luster and a white streak, with a specific gravity of 3.5. It is, however, very rare, and only occurs in kimberlite igneous rocks—the best sources are found in South and West Africa, Russia, Brazil, India, Australia, and the USA.

Carbon C **GRAPHITE**

G raphite is a soft, black form of pure elemental
carbon. Chemically, it is the same as diamond,
both being isotopes and polymorphs, which given their
widely differing properties is, at first, counterintuitive.
Graphite can occur as thin flakes or in a massive form,
and is often associated with quartz, calcite, tourmaline,
and mica; it is sometimes found as nodules inside iron
meteorites. In the field it is relatively easily identified,
with molybdenite being the most similar mineral—their
weights and streaks are entirely different, however, and
so confusion should not arise. Graphite is formed by the
metamorphosis of carbon-bearing materials, especially
those of an organic origin, such as coal. It has a metallic
to dull luster and a gray-black streak.

Color: Gray-black

Hardness: 1–2

Cleavage: Perfect in one direction

Fracture: Flaky

Crystals: Opaque, hexagonal

Specific Gravity: 2.2

Occurrence: New York and Texas,
USA; Russia; Mexico;
Greenland and India

NATIVE SULPHUR
Sulphur S

Sulphur is a yellow crystalline element that occurs in three different ways—as the native form, and as a wide variety of sulphide or sulphate compounds. Good specimens of native sulphur are very attractive, and are consequently highly sought after by collectors. Pure sulphur can be formed by the action of bacteria on sulphate minerals, as well as by the evaporation of volcanic gases or by geologic processes. Extensive deposits created by three of these are exploited for industrial extraction, since sulphur is an important constituent of a large number of commercial products, including fertilizers, explosives, and pesticides.

Composition: Sulphur

Color: Vivid yellow

Hardness: 2

Cleavage: Poor

Fracture: Conchoidal to uneven

Crystals: Transparent to translucent, orthorhombic

Specific Gravity: 2–2.1

Luster: Vitreous to resinous or dull

Streak: Yellow

Occurrence: Michigan and Ohio, USA;
Sicily, Poland, and Chile

HALIDES

The halide minerals are those which are composed of metals and one or more of the halogen group of elements. The naturally occurring examples of this group are fluorine, chlorine, bromine, and iodine—there is another member called astatine, but as this highly radioactive substance only has a half-life of just over eight hours, it has no mineral forms. Most halides are soft, transparent, and have a low density with good cleavage. The two best known examples of halide minerals are Fluorite, which is composed of Calcium Fluoride, CaF_2, and Halite, which is made up of Sodium Chloride, NaCl. Both have cubic crystal structures with a high order of symmetry, and these often occur as very interesting mineral specimens—consequently, they are popular with collectors as display pieces.

Sylvite is a halide mineral that is very similar to Halite—it is composed of potassium chloride, KCl, and forms when highly saturated saline waters evaporate. It was first found on Mount Vesuvius, in Italy, in 1832 by a Dutch scientist, and was thereafter named after him. In some areas it has accumulated over time in sufficient quantities to be commercially extracted for use as an agricultural fertilizer. It is a crystalline substance that is typically colorless or white. When impurities are present, however, it may be gray, red, brown, or yellow.

FLUORITE
Calcium Fluoride CaF$_2$

Fluorite—sometimes referred to as "Blue John"—occurs as cubic crystals as well as inclusions in other rocks, such as granite. It can be found in many places around the world, from Europe to North America. In the United States, deposits occur in Arizona, Colorado, Illinois, Kentucky, Missouri, New Hampshire, New Mexico, New York, Ohio, Oklahoma, and Texas. Fluorite is often associated with galena, sphalerite, barite, quartz, and calcite. The specimen seen here has cubic fluorite crystals bound together with octahedral galena crystals. The mineral's name comes from the fact that under ultra-violet light, it fluoresces strongly.

Composition: Calcium Fluoride

Color: From colorless, to white, blue, purple, blue-green, green, yellow, pink, or red

Hardness: 4

Cleavage: Perfect

Fracture: Uneven

Crystals: Transparent to translucent; isometric

Specific Gravity: 3.1

Luster: Vitreous to pearly

Streak: White

Occurrence: Widespread; major deposits in Germany, Austria, Switzerland, England, Norway, Mexico, Canada, and the United States

HALITE
Sodium Chloride NaCl

Halite, which is also known as rock salt, forms either cubic crystals or massive deposits. The crystal structures are cubic, and can be very attractive as mineral specimens. It forms from the evaporation of brine—either from the ocean or from inland lakes. The salt can eventually accumulate in vast layers, and over time these may be buried by mud or sand and end up as thick geologic strata. Many of these are mined commercially. Although halite is typically colorless or white, it can be permeated by various agents such as other minerals or bacterial matter, resulting in a wide variety of unusual color forms, ranging from blue or yellow to purple or pink. It is easily identified in the field due to its characteristic combination of taste, crystal shape, and cleavage.

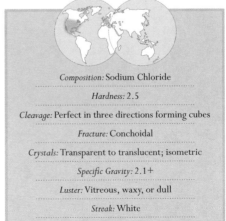

Composition: Sodium Chloride

Hardness: 2.5

Cleavage: Perfect in three directions forming cubes

Fracture: Conchoidal

Crystals: Transparent to translucent; isometric

Specific Gravity: 2.1+

Luster: Vitreous, waxy, or dull

Streak: White

Occurrence: USA, Germany, and France

OXIDES

Oxygen is the most common component in the Earth's crust, and so it is unsurprising that there are a lot of oxides in the mineral record. In fact, over 90 percent of all known minerals are strictly oxides of one form or another. To make academic organization easier, they are divided into various classes, more out of convenience than for any specific technical reasons. For instance, quartz, which is composed of silicon dioxide, is generally listed as a silicate, rather than an oxide. Where one group is considered to end and another starts is therefore often quite an arbitrary matter.

The oxides are a varied class of minerals, with many being important ores of industrially valuable metals. These include such examples as Hematite and Magnetite (iron oxides), Cassiterite (tin oxide), Bauxite (aluminium oxide), Chromite (iron magnesium chromium oxide), and Pyrolusite (manganese dioxide). Some of these are very common minerals—Hematite, for instance, is responsible in some areas for much of the red-brown coloration of the soil. Recent studies have also shown that it is widespread on the surface of the planet Mars.

Not all oxides are sought after as ores—ruby, for instance, has a number of commercial applications.

HEMATITE
Iron (III) Oxide Fe₂O₃

Hematite has been used as an important ore for the production of iron and steel for several thousand years. It is thought this first arose in the Near East and India during the middle Bronze Age. Hematite has also been used as a pigment in paints, and in more recent times the more attractive specimens have been sought by mineral collectors. It often occurs, as seen here, in botryoidal forms—these are usually referred to as "kidney ores." Other forms include micaceous hematite (also known as "specularite"), which is composed of large numbers of tiny flakes, as well as Hematite Rose and Tiger Iron, both of which are named after their appearance.

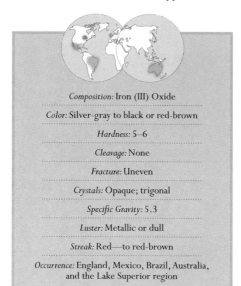

Composition: Iron (III) Oxide

Color: Silver-gray to black or red-brown

Hardness: 5–6

Cleavage: None

Fracture: Uneven

Crystals: Opaque; trigonal

Specific Gravity: 5.3

Luster: Metallic or dull

Streak: Red—to red-brown

Occurrence: England, Mexico, Brazil, Australia, and the Lake Superior region

RUBY *Aluminum Oxide Al₂O₃*

Color: Red to pink

Hardness: 9

Cleavage: None

Fracture: Uneven

Crystals: Transparent to translucent; trigonal

Specific Gravity: 4

Occurrence: Worldwide

Ruby is a variety of corundum (aluminum oxide) that has been colored red by trace quantities of chromium. The depth of coloring varies from a pale pink to a strong red. Although it is typically thought of as a valuable gem, fine examples are very rarely found. It occurs much more commonly as a very hard, but low-grade, translucent rock—it is, in fact, the second hardest natural mineral after diamond. These days synthetic versions are so close to the genuine article that it can be very difficult to determine which are real and which are not. Ruby has a vitreous to dull luster and a white streak.

Aluminum Oxide Al$_2$O$_3$ + Ca$_2$AlOAl$_2$(SiO$_4$)(Si$_2$O$_7$)(OH) RUBY-ZOISITE

R uby-Zoisite, which is also known as Anyolite or "Tanganyika artstone," is a mineral that is composed mostly of a variety of zoisite mixed with ruby—there may also be small amounts of hornblende. It is sometimes used for carvings, made into jewelry, or bought for mineral collections. It is usually found in metamorphic rocks, with the principal source being a mine near Longido, in northeastern Tanzania. In the few places where it occurs, it is often associated with minerals such as calcite, biotite, quartz, and garnets. The name Anyolite comes from a local Masai tribal name for the color green. This mineral has a pearly to vitreous luster and a white streak.

Color: Variable; typically

Hardness: Zoisite 6–7, corundum

Cleavage: Good in the longitudinal

Fracture: Uneven to conchoidal

Crystals: Transparent to translucent;

Specific Gravity: ~3.3 - 4

Occurrence: Tanzania

SPINEL

Magnesium Aluminum Oxide MgAl₂O₄

Spinel is chemically very similar to ruby, except that it also has magnesium in its crystal structure. Both get their typical red coloration from trace quantities of the element chromium, and while rubies are the more valuable, gem-quality spinel is still considered highly desirable. It usually occurs as octahedrons, with twinned crystals being a characteristic feature; however, other forms, such as dodecahedrons, are also found. It is often associated with the minerals calcite, corundum, dolomite, and garnets. Field identifications can be made by observing the crystal forms, as well as by checking the list of primary properties such as fracture, shape, specific gravity, and so on.

Color: Typically red, but also green, blue, purple, brown, and black

Hardness: 7.5–8

Cleavage: None

Fracture: Conchoidal

Crystals: Transparent to near opaque; isometric

Specific Gravity: 3.6–4

Luster: Vitreous

Streak: White

Occurrence: Myanmar, Sri Lanka, and Brazil

RUTILE

Titanium Dioxide TiO$_2$

The mineral Rutile is an oxide and major ore of titanium—a high strength, low weight metal that is used for a wide range of high-technology applications, from aerospace to auto racing. It forms striated crystal systems that are often twinned, with some of these being multiples that combine to make fascinating geometric structures. As a consequence of this, the more complex specimens are highly regarded by collectors. Rutile is also used to make jewelry and for carvings. It is often associated with a variety of oxide and silicate minerals, including barite, hematite, quartz, and tourmaline.

Composition: Titanium Dioxide

Color: Black, red-brown, yellow, or golden

Hardness: 6–6.5

Cleavage: Good in two directions forming prisms, poor in a third

Fracture: Conchoidal to uneven

Crystals: Transparent to opaque

Specific Gravity: 4.2+

Luster: Adamantine to sub-metallic; tetragonal

Streak: Brown

Occurrence: Brazil, Switzerland, Arkansas, USA, and some African countries

CASSITERITE *Tin Oxide SnO₂*

Color: Black, red-brown, or yellow

Hardness: 6–7

Cleavage: Good in two directions forming prisms, poor in a third

Fracture: Conchoidal to uneven

Crystals: Transparent to opaque; tetragonal

Specific Gravity: 6.6–7.0+

Occurrence: Bolivia, Cornwall

Cassiterite has been the primary ore of tin since the Bronze Age first began—and remains so. It occurs in two main ways; at primary sites and as alluvial deposits. The two main primary formations—those in Bolivia and Cornwall, England—have been more or less mined out. As a result, most tin extraction is now carried out from alluvial deposits that have resulted from cassiterite being weathered out of rocks and washed into river beds over geologic time. Cassiterite occurs in several different forms, from granular to botryoidal, fibrous, concretionary, and massive, as well as in a variety of crystal geometries. It has an adamantine or greasy luster and a streak which is typically white, but sometimes brown.

Iron Manganese Tungstate (Fe,Mn)WO$_4$ WOLFRAMITE

Wolframite is a dark-colored, heavy mineral that is one of the main ores of tungsten. It is, in fact, an intermediate between Huebnerite—Manganese Tungstate, MnWO$_4$ and Ferberite—Iron(II) Tungstate, FeWO$_4$. Since tungsten is an important constituent in many industrial processes and machine tools, wolframite is very important commercially. It is often associated with the minerals cassiterite, hematite, mica, pyrite, quartz, and tourmaline, and can be found as longitudinally striated crystals, columns and massive forms. The primary producer is China; however, it is also extracted in Colorado and other parts of the United States, as well as Russia, Korea, England, and Bolivia. It has a sub-metallic to resinous luster and a brown to black streak.

Color: Black, gray, or brown

Hardness: 4–4.5

Cleavage: Perfect in one direction

Fracture: Uneven

Crystals: Translucent to opaque; monoclinic

Specific Gravity: 7.0–7.5

Occurrence: China; Colorado and SW USA, Russia, Korea, England, and Bolivia

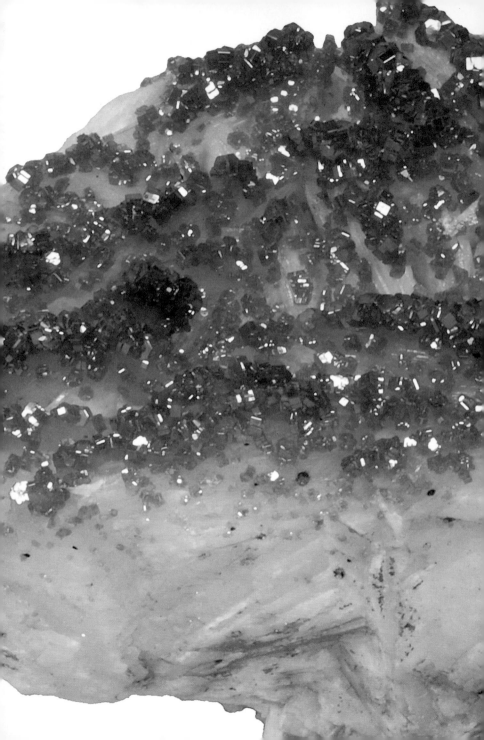

PHOSPHATES

The Phosphate class of minerals are naturally occurring inorganic substances which are primarily composed of the salts of phosphoric acid. There are more than 200 examples in the group, most of which are quite rare. The only one that is commonly found is Apatite, which is itself composed of three distinct calcium phosphate minerals—these are Fluorapatite, Chlorapatite, and Hydroxylapatite. Many members of the class have bright colors and/or interesting crystal forms, and so make excellent specimens for the collector's cabinet.

Some phosphate minerals are valued either for ornamental purposes or for use in jewelry. Turquoise, for example, which is a hydrous phosphate of copper and aluminum, has been considered to be a valuable gemstone since prehistoric times —the Ancient Egyptians were using it at least five thousand years ago. Amblygonite, which is a fluorophosphate mineral, is also used as a gemstone, but due to poor wear characteristics, has not been widely accepted in the marketplace. Lazulite (not to be confused with lazurite or lapis lazuli), is a little known semi-precious gemstone that is sometimes used in the jewelry trade. Other phosphates are commercially significant as ores of various metals—these include some rare minerals such as Autunite (hydrated calcium uranyl phosphate).

APATITE *A group of phosphate minerals* $Ca_5(PO_4)_3(F,Cl,OH)$

Color: Variable from green to yellow, blue, red-brown, or purple

Hardness: 5

Cleavage: Indistinct in one direction

Fracture: Conchoidal

Crystals: Transparent to translucent; hexagonal

Occurrence: Mexico, Canada, Germany, and Russia

Apatite, which is found in all the major rock types —igneous, metamorphic, and sedimentary—is actually made up of three distinct minerals. These are Fluorapatite, Chlorapatite, and Hydroxylapatite; the exact proportions of each vary between specimens, but they are almost always all present. The vast majority of apatite occurrences are as tiny grains spread throughout the parent matrix, but when large crystals form, they can be good enough to be used as gems. These are generally considered to be too soft for regular use in jewelry, however. Apatite has a specific gravity of 3.1–3.2, a vitreous to greasy luster, and a white streak.

A group of phosphate minerals Ca$_5$(PO$_4$)$_3$(F,Cl,OH) PINK APATITE

Pink apatite, which is the most commonly occurring member of the phosphate minerals, is found in most parts of the world, with specimen quality minerals mostly coming from Cerro del Mercado, Durango, Mexico, as well as Canada, Germany, and the Kola Peninsula, in Russia. Phosphorus is an important component of many commercial products and industrial processes. These include the manufacture of fertilizers, explosives, and pharmaceuticals, with the main sources being Apatite-rich rocks from such places as Algeria, Egypt, Israel, Morocco, and Tunisia. Pink Apatite has a specific gravity of 3.1–3.2, a vitreous to greasy luster, and a white streak.

Composition: Phosphate group

Color: Pink

Hardness: 5

Cleavage: Indistinct in one direction

Fracture: Conchoidal

Crystals: Transparent to translucent; hexagonal

Occurrence: Mexico, Canada, Germany, and Russia

VANADINITE

Lead Chlorovanadate Pb$_3$(VO$_4$)$_3$Cl

Vanadinite is a lead chlorovanadate mineral that is classified in the apatite group. It is an uncommon ore of vanadium —in the places where it occurs, it is often associated with lead deposit minerals such as barite, limonite, galena, and wulfenite. Specimens with good colors and a high luster are popular with mineral collectors, especially where the crystals are well formed; these generally occur as hexagonal systems. Vanadinite was first discovered in Mexico in 1801; however, at that stage it was considered to be a chromate mineral, as the element vanadium had not been identified.

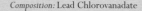

Composition: Lead Chlorovanadate

Color: Various shades of red, yellow, orange, gray, or brown

Hardness: ~3

Cleavage: None

Fracture: Uneven

Crystals: Translucent to opaque; hexagonal

Specific Gravity: 6.6+

Luster: Vitreous to adamantine

Streak: Yellow-white

Occurrence: USA (Arizona, New Mexico, and South Dakota), Mexico, Namibia, Zambia, Austria, Russia (Ural Mountains), Spain, South Africa (the Transvaal), Scotland, Morocco, Argentina

MIMETITE *Lead Chloroarsenate $Pb_5(AsO_4)_3Cl$*

Color: Typically yellow, orange, or brown; also green, colorless or gray

Hardness: 3.5–4

Cleavage: Imperfect

Fracture: Sub-conchoidal

Crystals: Transparent to translucent; hexagonal

Occurrence: Mexico (Mapimi), USA (Arizona), and Namibia (Tsumeb)

Mimetite, which is a member of the apatite group, is a Lead Chloroarsenate mineral. It is mined as a low grade ore of lead, as well as to supply the trade in mineral specimens; good examples are well regarded by collectors. It is typically yellow or close to it, but can also be anywhere between colorless and green. The crystals are rarely well formed, and this feature can be used to help with identification, along with its relatively high density and bright luster. It occurs in four basic forms—tiny needle-like crystals (as seen here), botryoidal crusts, small globular masses, and as medium-sized aggregations. This mineral has a specific gravity of 7.1+.

Lead Chlorophosphate Pb₅(PO₄)₃Cl PYROMORPHITE

Pyromorphite, which is a member of the apatite group, is a Lead Chlorophosphate mineral that forms close series with mimetite. Distinguishing between the two can be difficult, especially when the crystals are similar colors. It is used as a minor ore of lead, and is usually found in association with other lead-bearing minerals such as cerussite and galena, as well as limonite. Significant localities include mines in Idaho and Pennsylvania, USA, as well as at Mapimi in Mexico, along with others in Germany, England, and Australia. Pyromorphite forms barrel-shaped crystals that have hexagonal sections—these are usually green, but can also be yellow, orange, or brown. It has a specific gravity of ~7.0+, a resinous to adamantine luster, and an off-white streak.

Color: Typically green; also yellow, orange, or brown

Hardness: 3.5–4

Cleavage: Absent

Fracture: Uneven

Crystals: Transparent or translucent; hexagonal

Occurrence: USA (Idaho and Pennsylvania), Mexico (Mapimi), Germany, England, and Australia

VIVIANITE

Hydrated Iron Phosphate $Fe_3(PO_4)_2 \cdot 8(H_2O)$

Vivianite is a hydrated iron phosphate mineral that is usually a bottle green color. It is, however, very sensitive to light, and will darken to near black if left exposed. This is caused by the iron components within the crystal system changing their oxidative state. For this reason, specimens should be stored in the dark. The crystals themselves are usually flattened, but can also be fibrous, needle-like, prismatic, or massive—thin examples are flexible to a degree. Vivianite is often associated with the minerals siderite, sphalerite, quartz, and various others, and is sometimes found on or inside fossils such as shells or bones. It was first discovered in Cornwall, England in 1817.

Composition: Hydrated Iron Phosphate

Color: Blue, green, or colorless

Hardness: 1.5–2

Cleavage: Perfect in one direction

Fracture: Splintery

Crystals: Transparent to translucent; monoclinic

Specific Gravity: 2.6+

Luster: Vitreous

Streak: White or blue-green

Occurrence: USA, Russia, Ukraine, and England

ADAMITE

Zinc Arsenate Hydroxide $Zn_2AsO_4(OH)$

Adamite is classified as a member of the phosphate class, and is included in the arsenate subclass. It has no commercial value as an ore, but is extracted in many places for sale to collectors as specimen pieces. The botryoidal crystals fluoresce strongly under ultra-violet light, showing a bright green color, and even in daylight they are an attractive pale green and display a high adamantine luster. It is usually found on limonite, but is also associated with aragonite, calcite, mimetite, smithsonite, and many others. Adamite has similar crystal structures to olivenite and libethenite.

Composition: Zinc Arsenate Hydroxide

Color: Typically green; also yellow, white, or purple

Hardness: 3.5

Cleavage: Perfect in two directions

Fracture: Conchoidal

Crystals: Transparent to translucent; orthorhombic

Specific Gravity: ~4.4

Luster: Adamantine

Streak: White to pale green

Occurrence: Mexico (Mapimi), Greece, and USA (California and Utah)

WAVELLITE

Hydrated Aluminum Phosphate Hydroxide
$Al_3(PO_4)_2(OH)_3 \cdot (H_2O)_5$

Wavellite is a soft, pale green mineral that is composed of Hydrated Aluminum Phosphate Hydroxide. It has no commercial significance as on ore, but is collected for sale to the mineral specimen trade. It forms as a secondary material as small globular or botryoidal clusters of radiating needle-like crystals on parent matrix rocks such as limestone or chert. The main localities for it are Arkansas and Pennsylvania in the United States, as well as Bolivia and in parts of England. It has a vitreous luster, a white streak, and an uneven fracture.

Color: Typically green; also white, colorless, yellow, or brown

Hardness: 3.5–4

Cleavage: Perfect in two directions

Fracture: Uneven

Crystals: Transparent to translucent; orthorhombic

Specific Gravity: 2.3+

Luster: Vitreous

Streak: White

Occurrence: USA (Arkansas and Pennsylvania), Bolivia, and England

SULPHATES

The Sulphate class of minerals is made up of naturally occurring salts of sulphuric acid. Since they are usually insoluble in water, many—Gypsum (hydrous calcium sulphate) and Barite (barium sulphate) being good examples, are very common. Others, however, occur less frequently—Celestite, for instance, is a rare ore of strontium that is found in a few places in the United States, as well as Madagascar, Sicily and Germany. The vast majority are relatively obscure, with alabaster, anhydrite, barite, celestite, chalcanthite, gypsum, and selenite being the best known to those interested in the subject.

Overall, there are around 200 different kinds of sulphate minerals, with a few of them, such as the aforementioned gypsum, being of major commercial importance. This is extracted across the world for use as rendering plaster in the building industry, as well as for fertilizer and Plaster of Paris. This is used for making models and in healthcare for making support casts. Most sulphate minerals have a vitreous luster and are of moderate hardness. A few fluoresce under ultra-violet light, and this can be used as an aid to identification.

Many sulphate minerals have interesting and appealing shapes and/or colors, and this makes them popular with collectors as display specimens.

GYPSUM
Calcium Sulphate Dihydrate CaSO$_4$·2H$_2$O

Gypsum is a very common Calcium Sulphate mineral that is found in a wide variety of forms as well as in large beds of rock. These include alabaster and selenite, as well as several remarkable structural types, such as "desert roses" and large striated satin spars (as seen here). It occurs in most parts of the world, being formed from the precipitation of salt water, and is mined on a large scale in places like Mexico, Sicily, and the United States. It is a soft mineral that has transparent to translucent crystals that can be anywhere from colorless to white, tinged with any one of a number of pale red, brown, or yellow colors.

Color: Typically white, colorless, or gray, also red, brown, or yellow

Hardness: 2

Cleavage: Good in one direction, poor in two others

Fracture: Uneven

Crystals: Transparent to translucent; monoclinic

Specific Gravity: 2.3+

Luster: Vitreous to pearly

Streak: White

Occurrence: Widespread, especially Mexico, Sicily and USA (Utah and Colorado)

DESERT ROSE GYPSUM
Calcium Sulphate Dihydrate $CaSO_4 \cdot 2H_2O$

The name "Desert Rose" is given to unusual roseate structures composed of either gypsum and sand or barite and sand. As the term would suggest, they are found in arid deserts—these include the Sahara, the Sonora Desert in Mexico, and those of the south-western United States. They form as the result of the evaporation of mineral-rich saline solutions, with each of the "petals" being made up of individual crystals. These are usually orange or yellow, and are soft and translucent, with an uneven fracture and a vitreous to pearly luster.

Composition: Calcium Sulphate Dihydrate

Color: Typically orange or yellow

Hardness: 2

Cleavage: Good in one direction, poor in two others

Fracture: Uneven

Crystals: Translucent; monoclinic

Specific Gravity: 2.3+

Luster: Vitreous to pearly

Streak: White

Occurrence: Deserts such as the Sahara and those of the south-western USA and Mexico

ALABASTER

Hydrated Calcium Sulphate CaSO$_4$-2(H$_2$O)

Alabaster is a fine-grained form of gypsum —it is therefore a Hydrated Calcium Sulphate mineral. Although it is typically colorless, white, or gray, it can also be any one of a number of other colors, ranging from red to brown or yellow. The example seen here from Somerset in England has, for instance, a delicate salmon pink hue. It is very soft, and has been popular as a base material for carving ornamental stone sculptures such as statues for many thousands of years. It often forms in fissures in rock strata.

Composition: Hydrated Calcium Sulphate

Color: Typically white, colorless, or gray; also red, brown, or yellow

Hardness: 2

Cleavage: Good in one direction, distinct in two others

Fracture: Uneven

Crystals: Transparent to translucent; monoclinic

Specific Gravity: 2.3+

Luster: Vitreous to pearly

Streak: White

Occurrence: Widespread, especially Mexico, Sicily, Utah and Colorado, USA

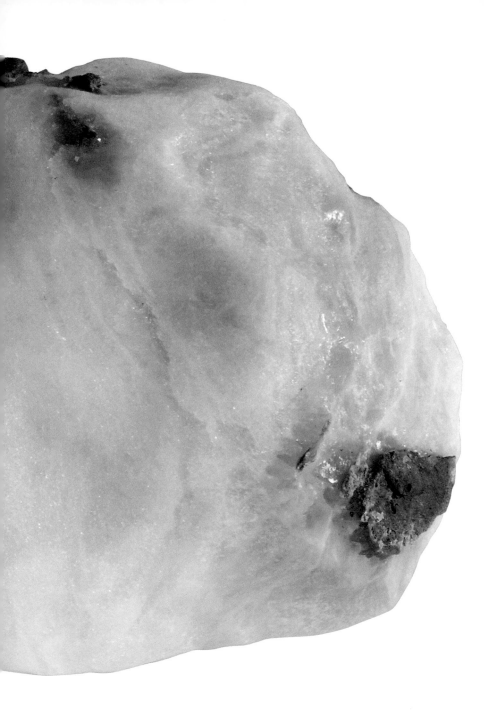

SELENITE   *Calcium Sulphate Dihydrate CaSO$_4$·2H$_2$O*

Color: Typically white, colorless or gray; also red, brown, or yellow

Hardness: 2

Cleavage: Good in one direction, distinct in two others

Fracture: Uneven

Crystals: Transparent to translucent; monoclinic

Occurrence: Widespread, especially Mexico, Sicily, Utah and Colorado, USA

Selenite is a form of gypsum that often occurs as completely transparent crystals. It does, however, also occur in white, gray, or with various hues caused by trace amounts of colored metallic components. It is named after the Greek moon goddess Selene, since it is thought that the pearly luster gives it a moon-like glow under certain lighting conditions. It often forms crystal twins of one sort or another—the example seen here is of a form known as a "fishtail twin." Others include swallowtail and spearhead twins, whereas some take on a spiral structure—these are known as "Ram's Horn Selenite." Selenite has a specific gravity of 2.3+, a vitreous to pearly luster and a white streak.

Hydrated Copper Sulphate CuSO$_4$ - 5H$_2$O CHALCANTHITE

Chalcanthite, which is Hydrated Copper Sulphate, is a bright blue mineral that is popular with collectors. These days many examples are, however, very convincing fakes produced by unscrupulous dealers to be passed off as the genuine article. It is very soluble in water, and quickly degrades if left in a damp atmosphere. It forms on or near the surface when copper-bearing solutions evaporate, however, and may well go through many cycles of being dissolved and then re-evaporating at a later date. In some places such as the Chuquicamata and El Teniente mines in Chile, it is a major ore of copper. Chalcanthite has a specific gravity of 2.2–2.3, a vitreous luster, and a pale blue to colorless streak.

Color: Bright blue

Hardness: 2.5

Cleavage: Poor

Fracture: Conchoidal

Crystals: Transparent to translucent; triclinic

Occurrence: Chile, Spain, England, Germany, Ireland, and many parts of the USA

BARITE or BARYTE

Barium Sulphate BaSO$_4$

Barite (which is also spelled "Baryte"), which is composed of Barium Sulphate, is a common mineral that is found across the world. It forms "blade" shaped crystals that are usually white or colorless—where influenced by trace quantities of metallic elements, however, these may be blue, green, yellow, or red. Barite is very similar to Celestite, and where there is some doubt, a flame test is the best identification method. Here, a small amount of the mineral is powdered and sprinkled into a naked flame. If this turns green, the sample contains barium, and so the specimen is barite. If it turns red, the colorant is strontium, and so the test piece is celestite. Barite has a specific gravity of 4.5, a vitreous, pearly, or dull luster, and a white streak.

Color: Typically colorless or white, but also blue, green, yellow, or red

Hardness: 3–3.5

Cleavage: Perfect in one direction, poor in another

Fracture: Conchoidal

Crystals: Transparent to translucent; orthorhombic

Occurrence: USA (Oklahoma, Connecticut, and Colorado), England, and Germany

CELESTITE
Strontium Sulphate SrSO4

Celestite, which is composed of Strontium Sulphate, is an attractive, pale blue mineral that is used both as an ore of strontium and for display specimens by collectors. Such pieces are especially sought after where they occur alongside other minerals that have strongly contrasting colors—sulphur being a good example. It is also associated with calcite, fluorite, gypsum, and strontianite, and some samples fluoresce under ultra-violet light. The example seen here is in the form of a hollow nodule, but it can also be found in fibrous and granular forms. Celestite can be confused with barite, but if a flame test burns red, then the sample contains strontium and the identification is confirmed. It has a specific gravity of 3.9+, a vitreous luster, and a white streak.

Color: Typically pale blue; also colorless or pale yellow, red, green, or brown

Hardness: 3–3.5

Cleavage: Perfect in one direction, poor in another direction

Fracture: Conchoidal

Crystals: Transparent to translucent; orthorhombic

Occurrence: USA (Ohio, Michigan and New York), Madagascar, Sicily, and Germany

SULPHIDES

The Sulphides are a very important class of minerals, as many are the primary ores of some of the most widely used metals in industry—these include lead, copper, nickel, and silver. One of the main by-products of several of the various extraction processes is sulphur dioxide. The sulphur dioxide is collected and then converted into sulphuric acid, itself an important ingredient in the conversion of many ores into metal.

Most sulphide minerals are dense, opaque, metallic substances that derive from igneous sources; however, some, such as cinnabar, orpiment, and realgar, form attractive transparent crystal systems. The sulphide mineral class generally also incorporates the arsenides, antimonides, bismuthinides, selenides, and tellurides.

Lead, which is an important industrial metal, is obtained from Galena—this is composed of lead sulphide (PbS). The largest source of copper is from Chalcopyrite—this is composed of copper iron sulphide ($CuFeS_2$). Nickel is extracted from Pentlandite—this is a mineral that is made up of nickel iron sulphide ($(Fe, Ni)_9S_8$). One of the ores of silver is Argentite, which is made up of silver sulphide, (Ag_2S)—this is a dark gray mineral with a metallic luster that is found in both veins and masses.

PYRITE

Iron Sulphide FeS$_2$

Pyrite, which is an iron sulphide mineral, is sometimes also referred to as "Fool's Gold," due to its shiny, gold-colored crystals. It is often found in association with calcite, fluorite, quartz, galena, sphalerite, and many other minerals. There are many different forms, including pseudomorphs of fossils, where the original material has been replaced by pyrite crystals, as well as nodules or flattened structures known as "pyrite suns." It is not used as a significant iron ore, but in the past has been mined for its sulphur content. These days it is mostly extracted for sale as commercial mineral specimens.

Composition: Iron Sulphide

Color: Pale yellow to brass-yellow

Hardness: 6–6.5

Cleavage: None

Fracture: Brittle or conchoidal fracture

Crystals: Opaque; predominantly cubic; also octahedral or pyritohedral

Specific Gravity: 5.1

Luster: Metallic

Streak: Greenish-black

Occurrence: Widespread; major localities include Russia, USA, Peru, Germany, and Spain

MARCASITE
Iron Sulphide FeS$_2$

Marcasite is an Iron Sulphide mineral that bears many similarities to pyrite; they are often confused with each other. Indeed, in many cases jewelry that is advertised as being composed of marcasite is actually made of pyrite. One method of distinguishing between them is by smell—marcasite sometimes gives off a sulphurous odor. Specimens that are left in damp environments tend to form a green oxidation fur, and eventually degrade into an unrecognizable powder. Examples that are stored in dry atmospheres can last for a long time, however, and are therefore popular with collectors.

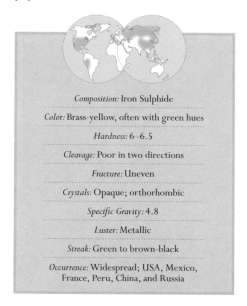

Composition: Iron Sulphide

Color: Brass-yellow, often with green hues

Hardness: 6–6.5

Cleavage: Poor in two directions

Fracture: Uneven

Crystals: Opaque; orthorhombic

Specific Gravity: 4.8

Luster: Metallic

Streak: Green to brown-black

Occurrence: Widespread; USA, Mexico, France, Peru, China, and Russia

LOLLINGITE *Iron Arsenide FeAs₂*

Color: Silver-white to grey,
darker when tarnished

Hardness: 5–5.5

Cleavage: Indistinct

Fracture: Uneven

Crystals: Opaque; orthorhombic

Occurrence: USA, Canada,
Republic of Congo,
Scandinavia, Austria,
Germany, Brazil

Lollingite, which is composed of Iron Arsenide, is classified as a sulphide. It is an uncommon mineral that is a silver-white color when freshly exposed, but this darkens considerably when tarnished. It is associated with several other arsenides, especially arsenopyrite, as well as calcite, siderite, sodalite, pyrrhotite, chalcopyrite, and others. The specimen seen here is also composed of Zinnwaldite and Gilbertite (a variety of Muscovite). Although it is a rare mineral, it is found in a number of different localities—these include Austria, Germany, Brazil, Norway, Sweden, Finland, Poland, and the USA. Lollingite has a specific gravity of between 7.1 and 7.5, a metallic luster, and a gray-black streak.

Lead Sulphide PbS GALENA

G alena, which is a silvery-gray mineral that is composed of Lead Sulphide, is the primary ore of lead, and is also one of the commonest sulphides in the Earth's crust. It is very soft, and demonstrates perfect cleavage in four directions, producing either cubic or octahedral crystals. It also occurs in granular and massive forms, often in association with calcite, cerussite, dolomite, pyrite, or sphalerite. The galena found in some locations has a relatively high silver content, making it the main commercial source of silver. Fine specimens are well regarded by collectors, especially where there is a good combination of luster (which is metallic to dull) and crystal shape. This mineral has a gray streak.

Color: Metallic silver-grey

Hardness: 2.5+

Cleavage: Perfect in four directions forming cubes

Fracture: Uneven

Crystals: Opaque; isometric

Specific Gravity: 7.5+

Occurrence: USA, Germany, Peru, Mexico, Zambia, and England

MOLYBDENITE

Molybdenum Disulphide MoS$_2$

Molybdenite, which is a soft, dark silvery-gray mineral, is the primary ore for the metal molybdenum. It occurs in a number of different forms—from thin sheet-like crystals to granular or massive structures. It is composed of molybdenum disulphide, which is an industrially important lubricant, and can also contain significant amounts of the element rhenium. Consequently, it is a valuable resource, and is mined in many places —prominent localities include the United States, Canada, Norway, and Cornwall in England. It is often found in association with the minerals anhydrite, pyrite, wolframite, chalcopyrite, quartz, fluorite, and scheelite, but is sometimes mistaken for graphite.

Color: Metallic silver-gray

Hardness: 1.5–2

Cleavage: Perfect in one direction, forming sheets

Fracture: Flaky

Crystals: Opaque; hexagonal

Specific Gravity: 4.7 to 4.8

Luster: Metallic

Streak: Blue-gray

Occurrence: USA, many Canadian localities, Norway, and Cornwall, England

CARROLLITE *Copper Cobalt Nickel Sulphide* $Cu(Co,Ni)_2S_4$

Color: Variable, from shades of gray to shades of red-brown

Hardness: 4.5–5.5

Cleavage: Indistinct

Fracture: Conchoidal to uneven

Crystals: Isometric

Specific Gravity: 4.5–4.8

Occurrence: USA and Republic of Congo

Carrollite, which is composed of Copper Cobalt Nickel Sulphide, is an uncommon mineral that originates in hydrothermal veins. It is extracted as an ore of cobalt, and is named after the locality where it was first discovered—Carroll County, Maryland, USA. The main source, however, is the Kamoto Principal mine in the south eastern part of the Congo basin, an area that is rich in valuable metal ores. It forms octagonal metallic crystals, often in association with other minerals, especially the copper ore, chalcopyrite. Good specimens with attractive crystals are sought after by collectors. This mineral has a metallic luster and a gray streak.

Zinc Sulphide ZnS SPHALERITE

Sphalerite, which is also known as Zinc Blende, is composed of Zinc Sulphide and is the principal ore of zinc. It is found in many places across the world, with the leading localities being sited in the United States, Australia, Italy, Spain, Myanmar, Peru, Morocco, Germany, and England. It occurs in a number of different forms, including massive, granular, botryoidal, fibrous, earthy, and as concretions. It has a complicated series of crystal habits, and is often associated with the minerals calcite, chalcopyrite, fluorite, galena, magnetite, pyrite, pyrrhotite, and quartz, as well as many others. Specimens with a high luster (which is adamantine, resinous, sub-metallic, or earthy) and good crystal structures are popular with collectors.

Color: Variable

Hardness: 3.5–4

Cleavage: Perfect in six directions forming dodecahedrons

Fracture: Conchoidal

Crystals: Transparent to translucent; isometric

Specific Gravity: 4

Streak: Yellow to yellow-brown

Occurrence: USA, Australia, Italy, Spain, Myanmar, Peru, Morocco

SILICATES

The Silicates mineral class is by far the biggest of the eight main groups. It is thought that about 90 percent of the Earth's crust is made up of a silicate of one form or another. They are divided into six sub-classes based on their internal geometries. These are the Cyclosilicates, Inosilicates, Nesosilicates, Phyllosilicates, Sorosilicates, and the Tectosilicates.

The Cyclosilicates generally have high hardness values, an attractive luster and good durability; examples include Beryl, Emerald, Dioptase, and Aquamarine. The Inosilicates include Rhodonite, Arfvedsonite, and Astrophyllite. The Nesosilicates are hard minerals with good optical properties. Many gemstones are found in this group. Examples of nesosilicates include Garnets, Staurolite, Topaz, Olivine, Kyanite, Andradite, Uvarovite, Titanite, and Phenakite. The Phyllosilicates are soft minerals. Talc, which is a phyllosilicate, has a Mohs scale hardness value of 1, making it the softest of all minerals. Others in the group include Apophyllite, Chrysocolla, Cavansite, and Muscovite Mica. The Sorosilicates include Epidote, Hemimorphite, Tanzanite, Thulite, Vesuvianite, and Zoisite. The Tectosilicates, which are often very common minerals, include Feldspar, Quartz, Amethyst, Albite, Labradorite, Sodalite, and Agate.

EPIDOTE

Calcium Aluminum Iron Sorosilicate

$Ca_2(Al, Fe)_3(SiO_4)_3(OH)$

Epidote, which is composed of Calcium Aluminum Iron Sorosilicate, is a complex mineral that has prismatic or tabular crystal structures with a single cleavage plane. The crystals are usually a similar shade of green to that seen in pistachio nuts—as can be seen here. These are often needle-shaped and striated with a vitreous luster. Epidote also occurs in massive, fibrous, and granular forms, and is often associated with the minerals actinolite, andradite garnet, biotite, calcite, hornblende, and many others. It is found in Austria, Italy, Mexico, and many states across the USA.

Color: Typically various shades of green—also brown or black

Hardness: 6–7

Cleavage: Good in one direction

Fracture: Uneven to conchoidal

Crystals: Transparent to translucent; monoclinic

Specific Gravity: 3.3–3.5

Luster: Vitreous

Streak: White to gray

Occurrence: Austria, Italy, Mexico, and many sites in the USA

ZOISITE *Calcium Aluminum Silicate Hydroxide* $Ca_2Al_3(SiO_4)_3(OH)$

Color: Variable

Hardness: 6–7

Cleavage: Good in one direction

Fracture: Uneven to conchoidal

Specific Gravity: ~3.3

Luster: Vitreous

Streak: White

Occurrence: Tanzania, USA, Switzerland, India, and Austria

Zoisite, which is typically a green color, is composed of Calcium Aluminum Silicate Hydroxide, and classified in the Sorosilicate subclass of the silicates. It belongs to the epidote group, and is primarily extracted for use as gemstones, mineral specimens, and for ornamental purposes. It forms transparent to translucent orthorhombic crystals as well as massive or granular systems. Although it is usually green, it can also be anywhere from colorless to purple, gray, yellow, brown, or pink. It is found in Tanzania, the United States, Switzerland, India, and Austria, often in association with andradite garnets, biotite, calcite, corundum, hornblende, and quartz, as well as other minerals.

Calcium Aluminum Silicate Hydroxide Ca₂Al₃(SiO₄)₃(OH) # TANZANITE

Tanzanite, which is a blue or purple variety of the mineral zoisite, was only discovered in 1967. It was thought that zoisite only occurred in low-grade forms, however, good specimens of Tanzanite have become established as valuable gemstones, and often display pronounced pleochroism. It is named after Tanzania, where it was first found, and to this day the only known locality for it is a single hill at a place called Merelani in the Arusha region of the country. Most of the specimens that come on the market have been heat treated to improve their color, as they are generally a pale green color when first extracted.

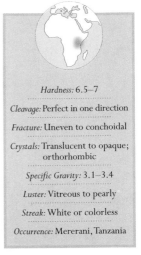

Hardness: 6.5–7

Cleavage: Perfect in one direction

Fracture: Uneven to conchoidal

Crystals: Translucent to opaque; orthorhombic

Specific Gravity: 3.1–3.4

Luster: Vitreous to pearly

Streak: White or colorless

Occurrence: Mererani, Tanzania

THULITE *Calcium Aluminum Silicate Hydroxide $Ca_2Al_3(SiO_4)(Si_2O_7)O(OH)$*

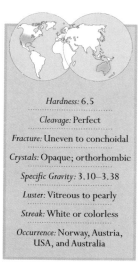

Hardness: 6.5

Cleavage: Perfect

Fracture: Uneven to conchoidal

Crystals: Opaque; orthorhombic

Specific Gravity: 3.10–3.38

Luster: Vitreous to pearly

Streak: White or colorless

Occurrence: Norway, Austria, USA, and Australia

Thulite, which is composed of Calcium Aluminum Silicate Hydroxide, is a pink form of zoisite that is also sometimes referred to as "Rosaline." It is found in a number of localities, including Lom in Norway, the Austrian Tyrol, Western Australia, and in North Carolina and Washington State, USA. It is an opaque, massive mineral with a vitreous to pearly luster that exhibits a perfect cleavage. Its soft pink coloration is due to trace quantities of manganese—this gives it an attractive look which has made it popular for ornamental use in the jewelry trade as well as for carvings.

Silicate Mineral Group $Ca_{10}(Mg,Fe)_2Al_4(SiO_4)_5(Si_2O_7)_2(OH,F)_4$ VESUVIANITE

Vesuvianite is a rare and complex sorosilicate mineral which is classified as a "silicate mineral group," rather than as any specific chemical compound. It is sometimes also referred to as "Idocrase," and is found in Canada, USA, Italy, Russia, and Switzerland. It was first discovered on Mount Vesuvius in Italy, which is where its name was derived. It occurs in several different forms—there is a blue version called Cyprine, a green gemstone type called Californite or Californian Jade, and various others. It is often associated with exotic minerals such as garnets, as well as more commonplace ones such as calcite and serpentine. This mineral has a vitreous, greasy, or resinous luster, and a white streak.

Color: Typically green

Hardness: 6.5

Cleavage: Poor

Fracture: Conchoidal to uneven

Crystals: Transparent to translucent; tetragonal

Specific Gravity: 3.3–3.5

Occurrence: Canada, USA, Italy, Russia, and Switzerland

HEMIMORPHITE
Hydrated Zinc Silicate Hydroxide
$Zn_4Si_2O_7(OH)_2 \cdot H_2O$

Hemimorphite, which is composed of Hydrated Zinc Silicate Hydroxide, is classified as a sorosilicate. It is extracted commercially as a minor ore of zinc, as well as to supply the specimen trade. It used to be known as "Calamine"; however, as this name was already being used for a different mineral, it was renamed. There are two main types of Hemimorphite—one forms as botryoidal crusts, while the other is made up of flat-bladed crystals with a vitreous luster. The main localities for it are the Santa Eulalia and Mapimi mines in Mexico, sites in New Mexico and New Jersey, USA, as well as others in England and Zambia.

Color: blue-green, green, white, colorless, brown, and yellow

Hardness: ~4.9

Cleavage: Perfect in one direction

Fracture: Conchoidal to sub-conchoidal

Crystals: Transparent to translucent; orthorhombic

Specific Gravity: 3.4+

Luster: Vitreous to dull

Streak: White

Occurrence: Mexico (Santa Eulalia & Mapimi), USA (New Mexico & New Jersey), England, & Zambia

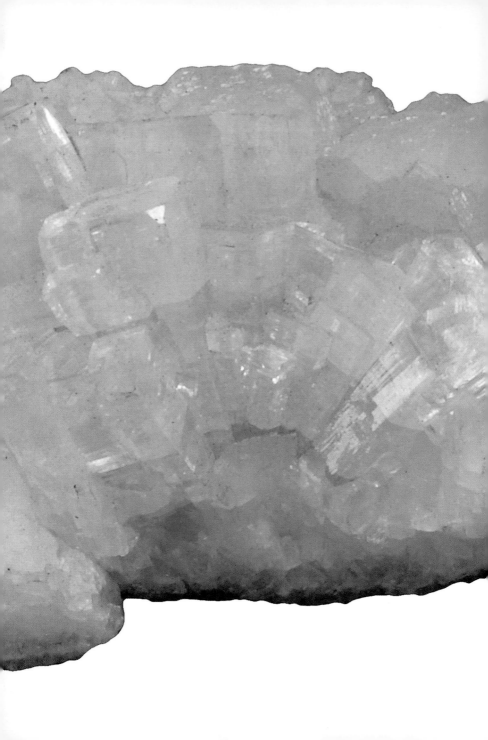

APOPHYLLITE

A phyllosilicate mineral group
$(K,Na)Ca_4Si_8O_{20}(F,OH) \cdot 8H_2O$

The name Apophyllite is given to three similar minerals that form what is referred to as a phyllosilicate mineral group. These are, in order of frequency of occurrence, Fluorapophyllite, Hydroxyapophyllite, and Natroapophyllite. Apophyllite crystals form in voids in lava, basalt, and metamorphic limestones, and have a pearly or vitreous luster. They can be anywhere from colorless to white, blue, green, brown, yellow, pink, or violet, and while they have a perfect cleavage, the fracture is uneven. Apophyllite has no commercial use other than as interesting mineral specimens for the collector—the example seen here is in a Stilbite (hydrated sodium calcium aluminium silicate) matrix.

Hardness: 4.5–5

Cleavage: Perfect

Fracture: Uneven

Crystals: Transparent to translucent; tetragonal

Specific Gravity: 2.3–2.4

Luster: Vitreous or pearly

Streak: White

Occurrence: Widespread, especially India, USA, Brazil, Scotland, Northern Ireland, Mexico, Canada, Iceland, Norway, Germany, Japan

CHRYSOCOLLA

Hydrated Copper Silicate
$(Cu,Al)_2H_2Si_2O_5(OH)_4 \cdot nH_2O$

Chrysocolla, which is composed of Hydrated Copper Silicate, is a vividly colored blue-green mineral that is popular with both collectors and for ornamental purposes. It usually occurs in massive forms —these can be botryoidal or encrustations, but can also be found as small inclusions in associated minerals. These include azurite, cuprite, limonite, malachite, and quartz. It is too soft for most jewelry applications, having a variable hardness that ranges from 2–4; it also breaks very easily. There is, however, a quartz-based variety that is known as "Agate-Chrysocolla"—this is much harder and can be used to make valuable pieces of jewelry. This mineral has a variable luster, from dull or vitreous to waxy or earthy.

Color: Various hues of vivid blue or blue-green

Hardness: 2 to 4

Fracture: Conchoidal

Crystals: Translucent to opaque; monoclinic or orthorhombic

Specific Gravity: 2.0–2.3

Streak: White to blue-green

Occurrence: USA, DR Congo, Israel, and England

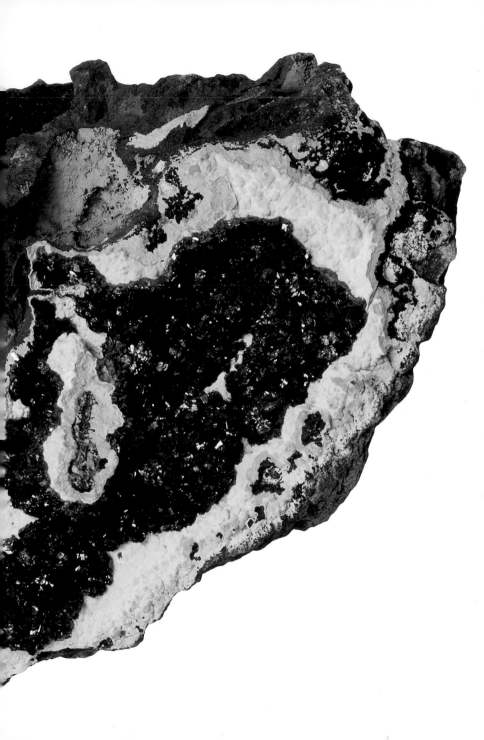

CAVANSITE

Hydrated Calcium Vanadium Silicate
$Ca(VO)Si_4O_{10}(H_2O)_4$

Cavansite is a rare vivid blue mineral that is classified as a phyllosilicate, and is composed of Hydrated Calcium Vanadium Silicate. It occurs as spherical clusters of radiating pointed crystals and was first discovered in 1967, in Malheur County, Oregon, USA. This site, and another in Poona, India, are the two primary sources. Although it contains vanadium—a valuable metal—Cavansite does not occur in sufficient quantities to become established as a commercially significant ore. Good specimens are, however, very highly regarded, and it has recently become very popular with collectors. This mineral has a vitreous to pearly luster and a blue streak.

Color: Blue to greenish-blue

Hardness: 3–4

Cleavage: Perfect in one direction

Fracture: Conchoidal

Crystals: Transparent to translucent; orthorhombic

Specific Gravity: ~2.3

Occurrence: Poona, India and Oregon, USA

MUSCOVITE MICA

Potassium Aluminum Silicate Hydroxide
Fluoride $KAl_2(AlSi_3O_{10})(F,OH)_2$

Muscovite Mica, which is composed of Potassium Aluminum Silicate Hydroxide Fluoride, is a common phyllosilicate mineral that is a major component of many rock types, including igneous, metamorphic, and sedimentary forms. Consequently, it can be found in many parts of the world. It has perfect cleavage, easily forming thin sheets—while it usually occurs as small flakes, in some places, notably India, Pakistan, Brazil, and certain parts of the United States, it can be found in large transparent pieces. These were once quarried for commercial use in high temperature or high voltage applications, but these days mica has been superseded by synthetic equivalents.

Color: White, silver, yellow, green, or brown

Hardness: 2.5

Cleavage: Perfect in one direction producing thin sheets or flakes

Fracture: Uneven

Crystals: Transparent to translucent; monoclinic

Specific Gravity: ~2.8

Luster: Vitreous to pearly

Streak: White

Occurrence: India, Pakistan, Brazil, and many parts of the USA

SPESSARTINE GARNET *Manganese Aluminum Silicate* $Mn_3Al_2(SiO_4)_3$

Color: Orange, reddish brown, brown, pink, or yellow

Hardness: 7

Cleavage: Absent

Fracture: Conchoidal

Crystals: Transparent to translucent; isometric

Specific Gravity: ~4.2

Occurrence: Pakistan, Madagascar, Brazil, and Sri Lanka

Spessartine Garnet is a nesosilicate that is composed of Manganese Aluminum Silicate. It is an attractive mineral that occurs in a variety of different crystals systems with either 12 rhombic or 24 trapezoidal faces, as well as in granular and massive forms. The main sources of high quality stones are in Pakistan, Sri Lanka, Madagascar, and Brazil, and a purple variety is found in the states of Colorado and Maine, USA. Other locations include Australia, Myanmar, India, and Israel. Spessartine Garnet is often associated with minerals such as beryl, feldspar, quartz, rhodonite, tourmaline, and topaz, as well as many others. It has a resinous, vitreous, or dull luster and a white streak.

Iron Aluminum Silicate Fe₃Al₂(SiO₄)₃ **ALMANDINE**

Iron Aluminum Silicate $Fe_3Al_2(SiO_4)_3$ **ALMANDINE**

Almandine is a form of garnet that is used for both industrial as well as ornamental purposes. The former includes various types of engineering abrasives, such as garnet paper, that are made from crushed almandine. They often form in high grade metamorphosed as well as igneous rocks when they are subjected to high temperatures and pressures. As a consequence of this they are relatively common, making them less desirable as gemstones, in spite of their good coloration, hardness, and lack of cleavage. Almandine has a resinous, vitreous, or dull luster and a colourless streak. The image seen here is of an Alaskan garnet that is embedded in a schist matrix.

Color: Red to brown

Hardness: 6.5–8.5

Cleavage: Absent

Fracture: Conchoidal to uneven

Crystals: Vitreous; isometric

Specific Gravity: ~4.3

Occurrence: India, Sri Lanka, Brazil, Austria, Norway, Australia, and several states in the USA

GROSSULAR GARNET

Nesosilicate Mineral Ca$_3$Al$_2$(SiO$_4$)$_3$

Grossular garnets are a calcium-aluminium form of the garnet mineral group. There are many different varieties, including californite, hessonite, hydrogrossular, Merelani, Transvaal Jade, tsavorite (which is also known as tsavolite), and viluite. These range from olive green to orange, red, brown through to various hues of purple, and can be found as massive through to well-formed crystals. They are often found in association with minerals such as albite, diopside, epidote, quartz, and vesuvianite, and occur across the world in a wide variety of different localities.

Composition: Calcium Aluminium Silicate

Color: Green

Hardness: 6.5—7.5

Cleavage: Absent

Fracture: Sub-conchoidal to uneven

Crystals: Transparent to translucent; isometric

Specific Gravity: ~3.6

Luster: Vitreous to resinous

Streak: Brownish-white

Occurrence: Mexico, USA, India, Germany, Norway, Russia, China, Australia, South Africa

UVAROVITE

Calcium Chromium Silicate Ca$_3$Cr$_2$(SiO$_4$)$_3$

Uvarovite, which is composed of Calcium Chromium Silicate, is classified as a nesosilicate member of the garnet group. It is a very attractive bright emerald green color, a property that is caused by the presence of chromium. It is formed by the metamorphosis of chromium-bearing siliceous limestones. Crystalline versions usually have either 12 or 24 faces—the better examples are used as unusual gemstones. It also occurs as granular and massive forms, often in association with the minerals chromite and serpentine. All three types are popular with collectors as mineral specimens.

Composition: Calcium Chromium Silicate

Color: Bright green

Hardness: 6.5–7

Cleavage: Absent

Fracture: Conchoidal

Crystals: Transparent to translucent; isometric

Specific Gravity: ~3.8 or less

Luster: Vitreous

Streak: White

Occurrence: Finland, Russia (Ural Mountains), United States (California), and South Africa

ANDRADITE *Calcium Iron Silicate Ca₃Fe₂[SiO₄]₃*

ANDRADITE $\text{Calcium Iron Silicate } Ca_3Fe_2[SiO_4]_3$

Color: Variable

Hardness: 6.5–7.5

Cleavage: None

Fracture: Brittle to sectile

Crystals: Transparent to translucent; isometric

Specific Gravity: 3.8+

Occurrence: Arizona, Russia, Italy, and California

Andradite is a nesosilicate member of the garnet group that is composed of Calcium Iron Silicate. There are many varieties of this mineral, each being distinguished by color. The green variety, which is sometimes used as a gemstone, is called Demantoid Garnet. The yellow version, which is also used by the jewelry trade, is referred to as Topazolite Garnet, and the black form is known as Melanite Garnet. The crystals grow in one of two types—a 12 sided rhombic dodecahedron or a 24 sided trapezoidal structure. Andradite also occurs in a massive form, often in association with mica, chlorite, diopside, and serpentine. It has a vitreous luster and a white streak.

Beryllium Orthosilicate Be$_2$SiO$_4$ PHENAKITE

Phenakite, which is also referred to as Phenacite, is a rare quartz-like nesosilicate mineral that has a high refractive index. This can produce such brilliance that faceted gemstones are sometimes mistaken for diamonds. It is well suited to use in jewelry as it has good hardness, no cleavage, and the better crystals are completely clear. Phenakite is composed of Beryllium Orthosilicate, and is typically colorless or white—sometimes, however, it has tints of brown, yellow, or pink. It is found in Russia, Brazil, the United States, and Norway, often in association with precious and semi-precious gemstones such as beryl, chrysoberyl emerald, and topaz, as well as smoky quartz. It has a vitreous luster and a white streak.

Color: Colorless or white

Hardness: 7.5–8

Cleavage: Absent or poor in three directions

Fracture: Conchoidal

Crystals: Transparent to translucent; trigonal

Specific Gravity: 2.9–3.0

Occurrence: Russia, Brazil, USA, and Norway

STAUROLITE

Nesosilicate Mineral Group

$(Fe,Mg,Zn)_2Al_9(Si,Al)_4O_{22}(OH)_2$

Staurolite, which used to be known as "Fairy Stone," is a complex mineral that is classified as a Nesosilicate Mineral Group. It is a common mineral that sometimes forms cross shaped crystals. These are the result of crystal twinning—indeed, its technical name is derived from the Greek words "stauros," which means cross, and "lithos," which means stone. It is typically a red-brown color, but can be much darker—even black—and is often associated with other metamorphic minerals such as almandine garnet, micas, and kyanite.

Composition: Nesosilicate Mineral Group

Color: Reddish-brown to brown or black

Hardness: 7–7.5

Cleavage: Poor in one direction

Fracture: Uneven to conchoidal

Crystals: Typically opaque, but also translucent; monoclinic

Specific Gravity: 3.7–3.8

Luster: Vitreous to resinous or dull

Streak: White

Occurrence: USA, Brazil, Scotland, Italy, and France

IMPERIAL TOPAZ *Aluminum-Fluorine Silicate Al$_2$SiO$_4$(F,OH)$_2$*

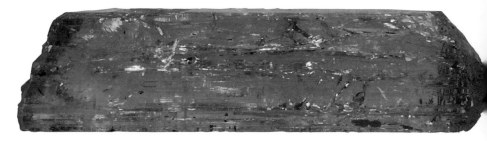

Color: Variable, from yellow to orange, red, blue ,or green

Hardness: 8

Cleavage: Perfect in one direction

Fracture: Conchoidal

Crystals: Transparent to translucent; orthorhombic

Specific Gravity: 3.4–3.5+

Occurrence: Brazil, Pakistan, USA, Russia

Topaz, which is composed of Aluminum-Fluorine Silicate, is a gemstone that is commonly used in the jewelry trade. Its attractive color, adamantine luster, and inherent hardness make it ideally suited for this purpose. It has perfect cleavage in one direction, and conchoidal fracture. Although it occurs as well formed, often longitudinally striated crystals, it can also be found in granular and massive forms, usually in association with minerals such as cassiterite, fluorite, mica, quartz, and tourmaline. The crystals can be any one of several different colors—golden variants, which are known as "Imperial Topaz," are amongst the most desirable forms. This stone has a white streak.

Aluminum-Fluorine Silicate Al₂SiO₄(F,OH)₂ BLUE TOPAZ

M ost naturally occurring topaz is colorless—such stones being commonly found in igneous rocks and high temperature veins, they are consequently not considered especially desirable. Blue Topaz, on the other hand, has significantly more value, but while it does occur naturally, most of the examples seen for sale are actually clear crystals that have been artificially irradiated and heated to generate the blue color. Depending on the exact treatment regime, any one of a number of shades of blue can be created, and the resultant gems are now the most commonly used stones in the marketplace. This stone has an adamantine to vitreous luster and a white streak.

Color: Blue

Hardness: 8

Cleavage: Perfect in one direction

Fracture: Conchoidal

Crystals: Transparent to translucent; orthorhombic

Specific Gravity: 3.4–3.5+

Occurrence: Brazil, Russia (Ural Mountains), Nigeria, Sri Lanka, Pakistan, Myanmar

OLIVINE (PERIDOT)

Magnesium Iron Silicate (Mg, Fe)$_2$SiO$_4$

Olivine, which is also known as Peridot, Chrysolite, and Evening Emerald, is a Magnesium Iron Silicate that is actually made up of two distinct minerals. These are Fayalite (Fe2SiO4) and Forsterite (Mg2SiO4); however, they are so similar that distinguishing between them is very difficult. Olivine is usually found in a granular, crystalline, or massive form, often in association with a variety of other minerals —these may include augite, chromite, diopside, feldspar, hornblende, serpentine, and spinel. There are many places where Olivine is extracted, all around the world. It is also found inside many iron meteorites. It has a vitreous luster and a white streak.

Color: Green to yellow-green, brown, black, or colorless

Hardness: 6.5–7

Cleavage: Poor in two directions

Fracture: Conchoidal

Crystals: Transparent to translucent; orthorhombic

Specific Gravity: 3.3 (Forsterite)—4.3 (Fayalite)

Occurrence: Egypt, Myanmar, South Africa, Russia, Pakistan, Norway, Sweden, France, Brazil, Germany, Mexico, Ethiopia, Australia, China, Hawaii, and the USA

KYANITE *Aluminum Silicate Al₂SiO₅*

Color: Variable, even within one crystal

Cleavage: Good in one direction

Fracture: Splintery

Crystals: Transparent to translucent; triclinic

Specific Gravity: 3.6+

Occurrence: USA, Canada, Brazil, Surinam, Russia, India, Kenya, England, Sweden, Germany, South Africa, Turkey, Bangladesh, and China

Kyanite, which is an Aluminum Silicate, is usually an attractive pale sapphire blue color and is also known as Cyanite and Disthene. It forms long, flat, prismatic crystals, often in association with other minerals—these may include andalusite, biotite, garnets, quartz, sillimanite, and staurolite. The specimen seen here, for instance, is surrounded by small red garnets. Good examples are prized by collectors. Kyanite has an unusual hardness property—it is around 4.5 in the longitudinal direction, but much higher—around 6.5—in the transverse direction. It has a vitreous, pearly, or dull luster and a white streak.

Aluminum Silicate Al$_2$SiO$_5$ **SPAR KYANITE**

S par Kyanite is an uncommon variety of the mineral that occurs as long spar-like crystals. These have the same characteristics as the more common forms, and are also a pale sapphire blue color and composed of aluminum silicate. Kyanite is extracted for several different commercial purposes, including for use as electrical insulators and various kinds of fine abrasives. It is found in many places around the world. Spar Kyanite has a vitreous to pearly luster and a white streak.

Color: Typically blue

Hardness: ~4.5

Cleavage: Good in one direction

Fracture: Splintery

Crystals: Transparent to translucent; triclinic

Specific Gravity: ~3.58+

Occurrence: USA, Canada, Brazil, Surinam, Russia, India, Kenya, England, Sweden, Germany, South Africa

TITANITE OR SPHENE *Calcium Titanium Nesosilicate CaTiSiO$_5$*

Color: Variable

Hardness: 5–5.5

Cleavage: Indistinct in two directions

Fracture: Conchoidal

Crystals: Transparent to translucent; monoclinic

Specific Gravity: 3.3–3.6

Occurrence: Pakistan, Italy, Russia, Canada, and USA

Titanite, which is also known as Sphene, is a Calcium Titanium Nesosilicate mineral that is named after its high titanium content. It forms good crystal systems that are often twinned—these display a strong adamantine luster. In strongly colored specimens this is enhanced with marked pleochroism—that is, different colors can be seen when it is viewed from different angles. Although this property results in very appealing gemstones, titanite's moderate hardness limits its utility for jewelry. It is, however, highly regarded by collectors for display specimens. It is found in association with various minerals including calcite, chlorite, feldspar, quartz, and zircon.

Complex Mineral Group LAZURITE/LAPIS LAZULI

Lazurite is classified as a complex silicate mineral group in the tectosilicate class. It is the main constituent of a massive rock called Lapis Lazuli—the other major components being pyrite and calcite. It has been mined for thousands of years, with the oldest sites being in a remote mountain location in Afghanistan called the Kokcha River Valley. In the ancient world it was prized for jewelry and other ornamental purposes, and in Europe it was used as the main pigment for ultramarine paints. These days it is still an expensive mineral, and well formed crystal specimens with good color are very valuable. It has a dull to greasy luster and a bright blue streak.

Color: Bright blue

Hardness: 5–5.5

Cleavage: Poor

Fracture: Uneven

Crystals: Translucent to opaque; isometric

Specific Gravity: 2.3–2.4

Occurrence: Afghanistan, Chile, Russia, Italy, USA

FELDSPAR

A tectosilicate mineral group; General formula:
$XAlSi_3O_8$ where $X = Ca, K$ or Na

Feldspar, which is classified as a tectosilicate mineral group, is a major constituent in the Earth's crust, comprising around 60 percent of its make-up. It is formed in igneous rocks by the crystallization of magma, and is also found in both metamorphic and sedimentary rocks. There are almost 20 different types of feldspar, with these being divided into two main groups—the plagioclase feldspars and the K-feldspars or alkali feldspars. The plagioclase feldspars include Albite, (Sodium aluminium silicate), Oligoclase, (Sodium calcium aluminium silicate), and Labradorite, (Calcium sodium aluminium silicate). The Kfeldspars include Microcline, (Potassium aluminium silicate), Sanidine, (Potassium sodium aluminium silicate), and Orthoclase (Potassium aluminium silicate).

Color: Off-white to pink or gray

Hardness: ~5.5–6.5

Cleavage: Good in two directions

Fracture: Conchoidal or brittle

Crystals: Translucent to opaque; monoclinic or triclinic depending on type

Specific Gravity: 2.5–2.7

Occurrence: Worldwide

RAINBOW MOONSTONE *Potassium Aluminum Silicate KAlSi$_3$O$_8$*

Color: Variable

Hardness: 6.0–6.5

Cleavage: Perfect in two directions

Fracture: Uneven

Crystals: Transparent to translucent; monoclinic

Specific Gravity: 2.5–2.6

Occurrence: USA, Mexico, Brazil, Germany, Tanzania, Madagascar, India, Sri Lanka

Rainbow Moonstone, which is also known as Water Opal, Girasol, and Fish-Eye is classified as being a tectosilicate in the feldspar group, and is a semi-translucent gemstone form of orthoclase feldspar. It displays an unusual adularescent sheen—this is a sort of shimmering reflection that is caused by particular geometries in its crystal structure. Its name is derived from this property. When polished, it can also exhibit another unusual lighting effect called "chatoyancy"—this is a sort of narrow cats-eye reflection. Those pieces which are not of gem-grade quality are often sold to collectors as mineral specimens. Rainbow Moonstone has a vitreous luster and a white streak.

Sodium Tectosilicate NaAlSi$_3$O$_8$ ALBITE

Albite, which is a plagioclase feldspar mineral, is composed of sodium tectosilicate. It is a light mineral that is commonly found in granite rocks, and often occurs in association with tourmaline, quartz, and muscovite micas. Since it crystallizes at a lower temperature than the other feldspars, it often forms at the same time and in the same place as much rarer minerals—the specimen seen here, for instance, has an aquamarine inclusion. As a result of this, albite often forms an important part of many mineral collections, albeit for secondary reasons. It has a vitreous to dull luster and a white streak.

Color: Typically white or colorless

Hardness: 6–6.5

Cleavage: Perfect in one direction and good in another

Fracture: Conchoidal

Crystals: Translucent to opaque

Specific Gravity: 2.6

Occurrence: Labrador, Canada, and the Scandinavian Peninsula

LABRADORITE

A Feldspar mineral ((Ca, Na)(Al, Si)$_4$O$_8$)

Labradorite is a plagioclase feldspar
mineral that is classified as a tectosilicate.
Polished specimens can display incredible
lighting effects called labradorescence—this
causes the colors to alter dramatically as the
angle of viewing changes. These can be bright
blue in one instant, and then golden yellow in
another. This behavior is caused by complex
light interactions between successive cleavage
layers, and the quality of specimens is mainly
judged on the range of colors exhibited.
Labradorite is found in Labrador, Canada, as
well as on the Scandinavian Peninsula, and
is often associated with the minerals biotite,
hornblende and pyroxene.

Composition: A Feldspar mineral

Color: Gray to black

Hardness: 6–6.5

Cleavage: Perfect in one direction, good in another

Fracture: Conchoidal

Crystals: Transparent to translucent; triclinic

Specific Gravity: 2.70–2.74

Luster: Dull to vitreous

Streak: White

Occurrence: Labrador, Canada and
Scandinavian Peninsula

SODALITE *Sodium Aluminum Silicate with Chlorine* $Na_4Al_3(SiO_4)_3Cl$

Color: Typically blue, but also white, gray, or green

Hardness: 5.5–6.0

Cleavage: Poor in six directions

Fracture: Uneven

Crystals: Transparent to translucent, massive specimens are opaque; isometric

Specific Gravity: 2.1–2.3

Occurrence: Canada, Italy, Brazil, USA

Sodalite, which is composed of Sodium Aluminum Silicate with Chlorine, is a rare tectosilicate mineral that is typically a dark royal blue color. It usually occurs in massive forms, and has been popular for use in ornamental applications ranging from jewelry to expensive carvings ever since it was brought to the wider market. It was first found in Greenland in 1806; however, much bigger deposits were found in 1891 in Bancroft, near Ontario, Canada. Since then many other localities have been discovered—these include Mont-Saint-Hilaire, Quebec in Canada, several sites in Arkansas, USA, as well as Bolivia, Brazil, Myanmar, Portugal, Romania, and Russia. It has a vitreous or greasy luster and a white streak.

MICROCLINE

Potassium Aluminum Silicate KAlSi$_3$O$_8$ **MICROCLINE**

Microcline, which is composed of Potassium Aluminum Silicate, is classified as a tectosilicate mineral in the feldspar group. A greenish-blue variety known as Amazonite—as seen here—is popular with mineral collectors as well as for use as a semi-precious stone by jewelers and as an ornamental stone. Microcline is a significant component of many granites, syenites (rocks that are similar to granites), and gneisses, and is often found in association with muscovite, plagioclase feldspars, and quartz. It can vary in color from off-white to pale yellow, pink, brown, or green. It has a vitreous to pearly or dull luster and a white streak.

Hardness: 6–6.5

Cleavage: Perfect in one direction and good in another, forming prisms

Fracture: Conchoidal

Crystals: Translucent to opaque; triclinic

Specific Gravity: 2.5

Occurrence: Colorado and North Carolina, other sites in USA; Russia; Norway and Madagascar

QUARTZ/ ROCK CRYSTAL
Silicon Dioxide SiO$_2$

Quartz, which is composed of Silicon Dioxide, is classified as a tectosilicate. It is the most common mineral in the Earth's crust, and can be found in a wide variety of different variants. These occur in massive and crystalline forms, with the latter being composed of hexagonal prisms which end with a six-sided pyramid. It is also often found as an encrusted lining inside rock voids and hollow geodes. There are a number of different commercial uses for quartz—these include as optical components in specialized instruments, as well as ingredients in paints, glass, and abrasives.

Composition: Silicon Dioxide

Color: Highly variable

Hardness: 7

Cleavage: Very weak in three directions

Fracture: Conchoidal

Crystals: Transparent to translucent; trigonal

Specific Gravity: 2.6

Luster: Vitreous to greasy

Streak: White

Occurrence: Worldwide

RED PHANTOM QUARTZ *Silicon Dioxide SiO$_2$*

Color: Variable

Hardness: 7

Cleavage: Very weak in three directions

Fracture: Conchoidal

Crystals: Transparent to translucent; trigonal

Specific Gravity: 2.65

Occurrence: Worldwide

The various types of quartz are mostly distinguished by color—for instance, purple quartz is known as Amethyst, pink forms are known as Rose Quartz, brown or gray variants are called Smoky Quartz, Milky Quartz is white, and clear examples are referred to as rock crystal. There is no specific name for the type seen here, which has red coloration as the result of trace impurities. Well formed specimens are popular with mineral collectors, and particularly clear crystals are used in the jewelry trade as semi-precious gemstones. Red Phantom Quartz has a glassy to vitreous luster and a white streak.

Silicon Dioxide SiO₂ ROSE QUARTZ

R ose Quartz is a pink variety of quartz that is
frequently used as a semi-precious stone in the
jewelry trade. It is also popular with mineral collectors
and for use as an ornamental stone. The attractive pink
coloration is due to trace quantities of iron, manganese,
and/or titanium; however, the crystals are only rarely
clear enough to be set as gems. Occasionally, rose quartz
occurs with needles of rutile running through it—these
can produce interesting lighting effects called asterisms.
The best quality specimens come from the Minas Gerais
mines in Brazil—the only source of good crystals—with
other sources including Germany, India, Madagascar, and
the United States. Rose Quartz has a glassy to vitreous
luster and a white streak.

Color: Pink

Hardness: 7

Cleavage: Very weak in three
directions

Fracture: Conchoidal

Crystals: Transparent to
translucent; trigonal

Specific Gravity: 2.65

Occurrence: Brazil, Germany,
India, Madagascar, and the USA

SMOKY QUARTZ
Silicon Dioxide SiO$_2$

Smoky Quartz, as its name would suggest, is a dark form of quartz. There are many varieties, such as Cairngorm, which is a dark brown to black form that is found in the Cairngorm Mountains in Scotland. Its coloration is caused by trace impurities of aluminum; however, a lot of commercial specimens have been artificially irradiated to darken the effect. Another variety is called Racoon Tail Quartz—this has black and gray stripes along its length. Yet another form is called Morion—this is very dark and opaque. Smoky Quartz is popular with mineral specimen collectors as well as a material for making carved ornaments, such as paperweights, eggs, statues, and so forth.

Composition: Silicon Dioxide

Color: Brown, smoky gray, or black

Hardness: 7

Cleavage: Very weak in three directions

Fracture: Conchoidal

Crystals: Transparent to translucent; trigonal

Specific Gravity: 2.65

Luster: Glassy to vitreous

Streak: White

Occurrence: Widespread; especially Brazil, Scotland, Swiss Alps, USA (Colorado), and many others

AMETHYST

Silicon Dioxide SiO$_2$

Amethyst is a type of quartz that has taken on a violet or purple coloration due to trace impurities of iron and aluminium. The exact hue and depth varies depending on its source. It can be found in many parts of the world, although few sites produce stones of significant value; the best quality specimens tend to come from Uruguay, Brazil, or southern Africa. It is often found lining the insides of geodes, especially those composed of agate; these are hollow, often spherical rock structures. Amethyst is often used for ornamentation, and has been used in jewelry and for ceremonial purposes since antiquity.

Color: Purple or violet

Hardness: 7

Cleavage: None

Fracture: Conchoidal

Crystals: Transparent to translucent; trigonal

Specific Gravity: 2.65

Lustre: Glassy to vitreous

Streak: White

Occurrence: Worldwide; Major producers are Brazil, Uruguay, Bolivia, Argentina, and Mexico. Zambia, Namibia, and various other African countries. Also Canada, Russia, Germany, Australia, Italy, and the United States

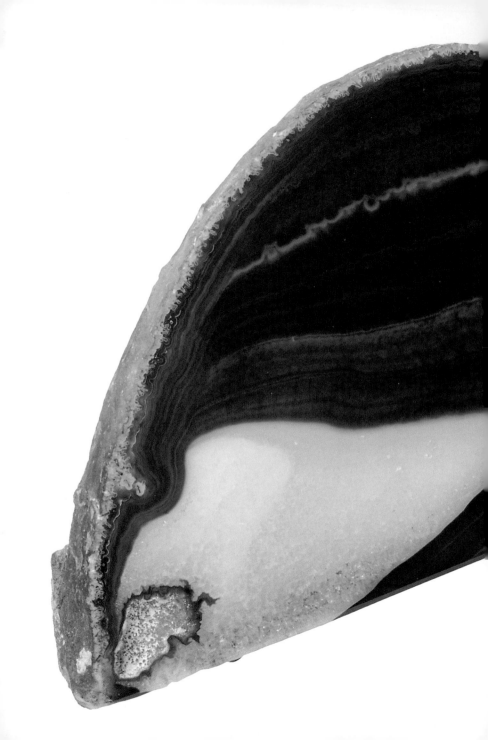

AGATE

Silicon Dioxide SiO₂

A gate is a type of quartz, and is therefore composed of silicon dioxide and classed as a tectosilicate. It is usually mostly made up of chalcedony, and there are many, many different varieties. These include blue lace agate, banded agate, moss agate, and onyx. It is very popular with the jewelry trade as well as for other ornamental purposes. Large quantities are prepared for sale as display pieces in a highly polished form—the majority of these are artificially dyed to enhance or even radically alter their natural coloration (as with the specimen seen here). Agate occurs in various forms all around the world.

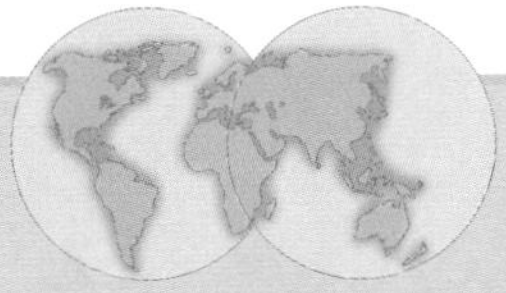

Composition: Silicon Dioxide

Color: Variable, from white to gray—also light blue to black, or with red to orange hues

Hardness: 7

Cleavage: None

Fracture: Conchoidal

Crystals: Translucent to opaque

Specific Gravity: 2.6–2.64

Luster: Waxy

Streak: White

Occurrence: Worldwide

CHALCEDONY *Silicon Dioxide SiO₂*

Color: Very Variable

Hardness: 6.5–7

Cleavage: None

Fracture: Conchoidal

Crystals: Translucent to opaque; hexagonal

Specific Gravity: 2.6

Occurrence: Abundant worldwide

Chalcedony, which is a microcrystalline form of quartz, is a tectosilicate mineral that has many distinct varieties. These are generally named after their color and include carnelian, sard, sardonyx, jasper, chrysoprase, and bloodstone. The most common varieties, such as flint, are usually a pale gray, or grayish-blue. The name Chalcedony derives from the ancient Greek town of Chalkedon, in what is now Turkey. It occurs in a number of different forms, particularly—as seen here—as encrustations which line the inside of vugs (voids in rock) and geodes, and has been used since the earliest times for ornamental carvings. Chalcedony has a vitreous or waxy luster and a white streak.

Silicon Dioxide SiO$_2$ # CHRYSOPRASE

Chrysoprase is a form of chalcedony that has been colored bright green by trace impurities of nickel. It is a relatively valuable stone that is used in jewelry and for ornamental purposes, although its color will fade if it is left in sunlight or is allowed to get too hot. It occurs in veins or as nodules, and is often associated with nickel and iron deposits as well as serpentine rocks. There is no cleavage, and it fractures in an uneven manner. Chrysoprase occurs in a number of parts of the world including Queensland and western parts of Australia, Germany, Russia, Poland, Brazil, and Japan, as well as Arizona and California in the United States. Chrysoprase has a vitreous luster and a white streak.

Color: Various shades of green

Hardness: 6.5–7

Fracture: Uneven

Crystals: Translucent to opaque; hexagonal

Specific Gravity: 2.6

Occurrence: Australia (Queensland & Western Australia), Germany, Russia, Poland, Brazil, Japan, and the USA (Arizona and California)

JASPER

Silicon Dioxide SiO$_2$

J asper is an opaque variety of chalcedony that has been colored red, yellow, orange, brown, or green by trace impurities of iron oxides—typically these are in the form of either hematite or goethite. It has been popular since ancient times for making ornamental items, and its vitreous luster helps polished pieces to look very attractive. It works easily, a property that was exploited by early hominids to make simple stone tools. Its lack of cleavage, uneven fracture, and relative hardness made it ideal for this purpose. Jasper occurs in many locations worldwide, particularly in association with Precambrian iron ore deposits.

Composition:	Silicon Dioxide
Color:	Red, yellow, orange, brown, or green
Hardness:	6.5–7
Cleavage:	None
Fracture:	Uneven
Crystals:	Opaque; hexagonal
Specific Gravity:	2.6
Luster:	Vitreous
Streak:	White
Occurrence:	Worldwide

SCAPOLITE
Silicate Mineral Group Ca4(Si,Al)$_{12}$O$_{24}$(CO$_3$,SO$_4$) and Na$_4$(Al, Si)$_{12}$O$_{24}$Cl

Color: Typically white, but most colors possible

Hardness: 5.5–6

Cleavage: Distinct in several directions

Fracture: Sub-conchoidal to uneven

Crystals: Translucent to transparent; tetragonal

Occurrence: USA, Norway, Italy, Mexico, Brazil, Madagascar, Switzerland, and Myanmar

Scapolite, which over the years has also been referred to as Wernerite and Mizzonite, is a generic term for a mineral series that ranges between Marialite and Meionite. Distinguishing between the various forms can be exceedingly difficult, due to the close similarity of their properties. It is sometimes used as a gemstone; however, although it can have attractive coloration, its lack of hardness and vitreous luster prevent it from being more desirable. It rarely forms complete crystals, and is more usually seen—as here—with uneven faces. Under ultra-violet light it fluoresces yellow, orange, or red. It has a specific gravity of 2.5–2.7.

Hydrous Calcium & Aluminum Silicate # HEULANDITE
$(Ca, Na)_{2-3}Al_3(Al, Si)_2Si_{13}O_{36} \cdot 12H_2O$

Heulandite, which is composed of Hydrous Calcium and Aluminum Silicate, is a tectosilicate that is named after a famous British mineral collector called John Henry Heuland. It is a member of the zeolite group, and is well known for its intricate crystal systems which can have either a vitreous or a pearly luster. They can be a variety of colors, from colorless to white, gray, green, pink, yellow, red, brown, or black, dependent on the levels of metallic impurities. Typically, these are made up of strontium, potassium, magnesium, and barium. Heulandite is found in many parts of the world, often in association with rare minerals such as apophyllite, prehnite, and tourmaline. It has a vitreous to pearly luster and a white streak, with a specific gravity of 2.1–2.3.

Color: Variable

Hardness: 3.5–4

Cleavage: Perfect in one direction

Fracture: Uneven

Crystals: Transparent or translucent; monoclinic

Occurrence: Australia, Brazil, Canada, Iceland, India, Iran, Italy, New Zealand, Russia, Sardinia, Scotland, Switzerland, and the United States

EMERALD

Beryllium Aluminum Silicate (Be$_3$Al$_2$(SiO$_3$)$_6$)

Emerald is a vivid green gemstone that can be very valuable if it is free from any inclusions or other faults; few examples, however, make this grade. It is a member of the beryl family, and gains its beautiful color from chromium, along with trace amounts of iron, or vanadium. The best quality gems come from Columbia, where there are nearly 150 mining locations. By far the biggest of these is at Coscuez, a site which supplies around three-quarters of Columbia's emeralds. They were also mined in historical times in Egypt and Germany. The specimen pictured here is partially embedded in parent rock known as "matrix."

Hardness: 7.5–8

Cleavage: Poor

Fracture: Conchoidal

Crystals: Hexagonal

Specific Gravity: 2.67–2.78

Luster: Vitreous

Streak: White

Occurrence: Columbia, Brazil, Zambia and Zimbabwe, Pakistan, India, Russia, Afghanistan, Australia, Madagascar, and from North Carolina, Connecticut, Maine, and New Hampshire in the USA

DIOPTASE

Hydrated Copper Silicate CuSiO$_3$_H$_2$O

Dioptase, which is composed of Hydrated Copper Silicate, is classified as a cyclosilicate mineral. It has a vivid blue-green coloration, which makes it very popular with mineral collectors. Although it is sometimes used as a gemstone, its cleavage is too marked, and it is not hard enough to be widely accepted for this purpose. It produces good rhombohedral crystals with a high vitreous luster—these may be transparent or translucent. Dioptase also occurs in massive and encrusted forms, often in association with calcite, cerussite, chrysocolla, dolomite, limonite, and other copper-based minerals.

Composition: Hydrated Copper Silicate

Color: Vivid green

Hardness: 5

Cleavage: Perfect in three directions forming rhombohedrons

Fracture: Conchoidal and brittle

Crystals: Transparent to translucent; trigonal

Specific Gravity: ~3.3+

Luster: Vitreous

Streak: Green

Occurrence: Namibia (Tsumeb), Zaire, Russia, USA (California and Arizona), and Chile

AQUAMARINE *Beryllium Aluminum Silicate* $Be_3Al_2Si_6O_{18}$

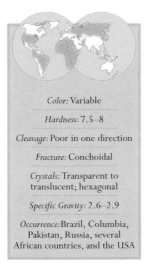

Color: Variable

Hardness: 7.5–8

Cleavage: Poor in one direction

Fracture: Conchoidal

Crystals: Transparent to translucent; hexagonal

Specific Gravity: 2.6–2.9

Occurrence: Brazil, Columbia, Pakistan, Russia, several African countries, and the USA

Aquamarine, which is a pale blue-green colored variety of beryl, is an attractive mineral that is classified as a cyclosilicate. It is composed of Beryllium Aluminium Silicate, but with trace impurities of iron compounds—these impart its subtle coloration. Most commercial specimens, however, have been heat treated to change them from pale yellow to blue-green, or to enhance and deepen the existing colors. It has a vitreous luster, and is often associated with calcite, mica, quartz, tourmaline, and some varieties of feldspar. Aquamarine is popular with collectors, especially when it is part of a larger and more interesting mineral specimen. It has a white streak.

Manganese Inosilicate (Mn,Fe,Mg,Ca)SiO₃ RHODONITE

R hodonite, which is classified as an inosilicate mineral in the pyroxene group, is typically a strong pink or pale red color. It can, however— dependent on the relative amounts of trace impurities of iron, magnesium, calcium, or zinc—also be a gray or black color, especially if it has been exposed for any length of time. Rhodonite is usually reasonably easy to identify, but can be confused with rhodochrosite and pyroxmangite. The former can be distinguished, as it often has white streaks of calcite running through it, but the latter is more difficult, sometimes needing x-ray analysis. Rhodonite has a vitreous, dull, or pearly luster and a white streak. Its specific gravity is 3.4–3.7.

Color: Typically pink, but also red, orange, gray, or black

Hardness: 5.5–6.5

Cleavage: Perfect in two directions forming prisms

Fracture: Conchoidal

Crystals: Translucent to transparent; triclinic

Occurrence: Russia (Urals), Australia (Broken Hill), Sweden, Brazil, and USA

ARFVEDSONITE

Sodium Iron Magnesium Silicate Hydroxide

$Na_3(Fe, Mg)_4FeSi_8O_{22}(OH)_2$

Arfvedsonite, which is classified as an inosilicate in the amphibole group, is composed of Sodium Iron Magnesium Silicate Hydroxide, and named after the Swedish chemist Johan A. Arfvedson. It is an important constituent in many rocks, and sometimes forms long crystals—these may be prismatic, needle-like, or tabular. It also occurs in fibrous, lamellar, and massive forms, and may be associated with a large number of other minerals, many of which are somewhat obscure. The better known ones include mica, and various kinds of feldspars and feldspathoids. The only use for Arfvedsonite is as mineral specimens.

Color: Greenish-black, gray, or black

Hardness: 5.5–6

Cleavage: Perfect in two directions

Fracture: Uneven to sub-conchoidal

Crystals: Translucent to opaque; monoclinic

Specific Gravity: 3.1–3.5

Luster: Vitreous to dull or silky

Streak: Dark blue-gray

Occurrence: Canada, Greenland, Russia, Germany, Norway, USA (Colorado and New Hampshire)

ASTROPHYLLITE
Potassium Sodium Iron Manganese Titanium Silicate Hydroxide (K, Na)₃(Fe, Mn)₇Ti₂(SiO₃)₈(O, OH)₇

Potassium Sodium Iron Manganese Titanium Silicate Hydroxide $(K, Na)_3(Fe, Mn)_7 Ti_2 (SiO_3)_8 (O, OH)_7$

Hardness: 3

Cleavage: Perfect in one direction

Fracture: Uneven

Crystals: Translucent to opaque; triclinic

Specific Gravity: 3.3–3.4

Streak: Pale yellow-white

Occurrence: Russia (Kola Peninsula), USA (Colorado), and Canada (Quebec)

Astrophyllite, which is classified as an inosilicate in the astrophyllite group, is composed of Potassium Sodium Iron Manganese Titanium Silicate Hydroxide. It is a rare and complex mineral that is only found in a few locations, including the Kola Peninsula in Russia, Colorado in the United States, and near Quebec in Canada. It has perfect cleavage in one direction, a vitreous, metallic, sub-metallic or pearly luster, and can vary from yellow to yellow-brown, golden or greenish brown. It has no commercial use other than as mineral specimens, and is often associated with quartz, various feldspars, nepheline, and mica.

Sodium Lithium Aluminum Borosilicate INDICOLITE
$Na(LiAl)_3Al_6Si_6O_{18}(BO_3)_3(OH)_4$

Indicolite, which is a blue variety of Elbaite, is the rarest and most desirable member of the tourmaline family. It is prized as a valuable gemstone—the combination of a good sparkle and being strongly pleochroic gives a very pleasing aspect. Depending on the viewing angle, it can appear to be anywhere from azure to dark blue. This coloration is due to trace impurities of iron and manganese. It is formed as the result of volcanic activity, and is found in many places around the world, with the best specimens coming from the Minas Gerais mines in Brazil. This stone has a vitreous luster and a colorless streak.

Color: Various shades of blue

Hardness: 7–7.5

Cleavage: None

Fracture: Conchoidal to uneven

Crystals: Trigonal

Specific Gravity: ~3.0

Occurrence: Brazil, Myanmar, India, Italy, Kenya, Madagascar, Namibia, Russia, Sri Lanka, Tanzania, and the USA

TOURMALINE

Complex Mineral Group (Ca,K,Na)(Al,Fe,Li,M g,Mn)$_3$(Al,Cr,Fe,V)$_6$(BO$_3$)$_3$(Si,Al,B)$_6$O$_{18}$(OH,F)$_4$

Tourmaline is classified as a complex mineral group—there are many varieties with a wide range of constituents, typically including Calcium, Potassium, Sodium, Aluminum, Iron, Lithium, Magnesium, Manganese, Chromium, Vanadium, Boron, Silicon, Oxygen, Hydrogen, and Fluorine. Tourmaline occurs in many rock systems, including granites, marbles, sandstone, and various kinds of schist, in many different forms. These include black, green, pink, purple, brown, or red and green varieties, the crystals of which are pleochroic, and have a vitreous to resinous luster. The finer examples of Elbaite and Uvite are used as gemstones, whereas schorl is seen commonly as the black specs in granite; there are also many other kinds of tourmaline, most of which are prized by collectors.

Hardness: 7–7.5	
Cleavage: Indistinct	
Fracture: Brittle and uneven; conchoidal	
Crystals: Very variable; from granular form in granite, to parallel and elongated crystals	
Specific Gravity: 3.0–3.25	
Streak: White	
Occurrence: Worldwide in association with granite, marble, sandstone, and schist	

ORGANICS

There are several definitions as to exactly what constitutes an organic mineral, with some regimes disallowing anything except inorganic materials. For the purposes of this publication, organic minerals are taken to include those materials that have an organic component in their make-up and have undergone some form of geologic process. Many different chemical compound types fit into this classification system, including acetates, citrates, cyanates, formates, and oxalates, as well as hydrocarbons. Examples of the organic minerals include Coal, Peat, Amber, and Jet as well as:

Abelsonite—$Ni[C_{32}H_{36}N_4]$—a Nickel Porphyrine derivative; Carpathite—$C_{24}H_{12}$—a Polycyclic Aromatic Hydrocarbon; Evenkite—$C_{24}H_{50}$—n-tetracosane; Fichtelite—$C_{19}H_{34}$—Dimethyl-isopropyl-perhydrophenanthrene; Melanophlogite —$46SiO_2 \cdot 6(N_2,CO_2) \cdot 2(CH_4,N_2)$—Silicon Oxide with organic compounds; Mellite—$Al_2[C_6(COO)_6] \cdot 16H2O$ —Aluminum Mellitate (benzene hexacarboxylate) Hydrate; Moolooite—$Cu[O \mid C_2O_4] \cdot 4H_2O$—a Hydrated Copper Oxalate; Oxammite—$(NH_4)_2[C_2O_4] \cdot H_2O$—Oxalate and Ammonium ions; Wheatleyite—$Na2Cu[C2O4]2 \cdot 2H2O$ —a Sodium Copper Salt of Oxalic Acid; Whewellite —$Ca[C_2O_4] \cdot H_2O$—Hydrated Calcium Oxalate.

COAL

Color: Dark brown to black

Origin: Carboniferous

Grain Size: N/A

Occurrence: Worldwide

Coal is an organic material that is formed by the fossilization of plant material, typically that of swamp areas. The process begins when plants or trees die and are then covered by mud. Over time, this gets buried by successive layers of soil, and eventually it is carbonized by heat and pressure into coal. There are many different grades, and most are very valuable fuels—consequently, they are extracted for commercial use the world over. The best known form is anthracite—this is a hard, black substance that is primarily used for heating domestic and commercial buildings. Another variety is bituminous coal, which is mainly used to generate electricity in power stations. The specimen seen here is of a variety known as Culm Coal.

COAL BRECCIA

C oal breccias are rocks that are composed of a mixture of coal fragments with a parent matrix material. They can be formed in a number of ways, most of which involve a coal bed being disrupted by some kind of geologic disturbance, and the resulting pieces being mixed with other materials and then deposited as a sedimentary layer. Examples of these disruptive events include mud slides, avalanches, tsunamis, and earthquakes. The distance that the coal fragments have traveled from their original location can sometimes be inferred by their density, as well as by their size and shape—the smaller the pieces of coal breccia and the more rounded their edges, the further they have traveled.

Color: Variable depending on the parent matrix material

Origin: Carboniferous

Grain Size: Variable

Occurrence: Worldwide

FOSSILIZED PEAT

Color: Dark brown to black

Origin: Botanical

Grain Size: N / A

Occurrence: Worldwide

eat is an organic material that forms when wetland mosses die and become buried by mud. Gradually, it becomes fossilized and compacted by weight of material accumulating above it—over extended periods of geologic time, it eventually turns into coal. The specimen seen here is an example of an early stage in this process. It was recovered from the remains of a post-Ice Age forest that had become buried, and then exposed some ten thousand years later by the action of the sea. Peat is found in many places—currently, peatlands cover about three percent of the world's land mass.

JET

Jet is an organic material that is composed of fossilized wood, typically of a tree species called Araucaria that lived in the Jurassic era, about 150–180 million years ago. This closely resembled the Monkey-puzzle tree that we see growing today. The fossils formed when the trees died and were washed out to sea—their remains then sank into the mud below, where they were preserved by the lack of oxygen. Before long, further mud accumulated, and they became compressed and eventually incorporated into the sedimentary rock that surrounded them. Today, Jet is a sought-after material for use in jewelry and for other ornamental purposes.

Color: Dark brown to black

Origin: Marine

Grain Size: N / A

Occurrence: Worldwide

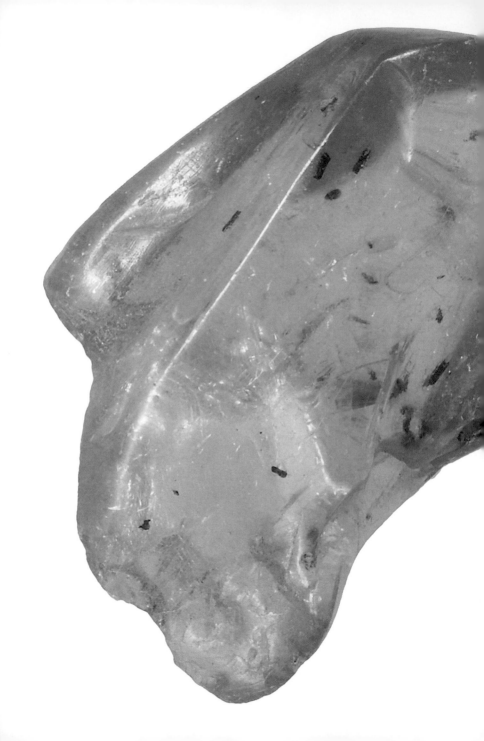

AMBER

Succinic Acid $C_{10}H_{16}O$

Amber is a well-known organic material that is composed of fossilized tree resin. It is sought after both for ornamental purposes, such as gemstones, as well as by specimen collectors. Since resin is inherently sticky, amber often contains particles or objects that became stuck to it and then entombed by it. Consequently, they are many millions of years old. The most highly prized examples are those which have small creatures trapped inside them. These may be insects—beetles, ants, flies—spiders, or even small reptiles or amphibians. Genuine amber is a valuable material, but is often faked by unscrupulous dealers.

Color: Amber yellow to orange

Hardness: 2+

Cleavage: None

Fracture: Conchoidal

Crystals: Transparent to translucent

Specific Gravity: ~1.1

Luster: Resinous

Streak: White

Origin: Continental

Occurrence: The Baltic, Venezuela, Russia, Romania, Myanmar, USA, & Dominican Republic

METAMORPHIC ROCKS

The rocks that are classified as metamorphic are those which have undergone physical changes as the result of experiencing increased pressures and/or increased temperatures at some point in their existence. They make up a major part of the Earth's crust, and are formed deep within it as the result of the extreme heat and pressure present at great depths. A large part of this is due to the weight of the rocks above; however, if magma makes its way into their vicinity, this will also cause localized heating and consequent pressure increases. Any rock type can be altered in such a manner—sedimentary, igneous, and even those which have already been previously metamorphosed. The degree of change can vary tremendously, from that which is barely noticeable to that which is extreme, where the chemistry may well have been significantly modified. A good example is where limestone is compressed and heated over geological time, and becomes metamorphosed into marble. As part of this process, the small calcite minerals melt and recrystallize in a larger form. Examples of metamorphic rocks include gneiss, marble, schist, and slate.

SCHIST

Color: Brown to gray

Origin: Mountain ranges

Grain Size: Medium

Occurrence: Worldwide

Schists are metamorphic rocks that are composed of a variety of minerals including quartz, mica, feldspar, hornblende, chlorite, graphite, and talc. These are in the form of thin flakes that can be easily separated from each other—indeed the name "schist" is from the Greek term for "split." Most are derived from sedimentary materials like clay or mud that has then undergone a series of metamorphic processes. Others started out as igneous rocks such as basalt; however, it can be very difficult, if not impossible, to determine the exact provenance of those examples that have undergone significant metamorphic changes.

MICA SCHIST

Mica Schist is a relatively light rock that is derived from sedimentary sources and mostly composed of mica and quartz. It is often found in association with rocks that are made up of limestone or gneiss, and like other forms of schist, it is made up of thin flakes that can be easily split away from one another. The mica component can be made up of any one of a number of different types, with muscovite and biotite being the most common. Several interesting minerals can occur in mica schist, with specimens containing things like garnets, kyanite, or staurolite being sought after by collectors.

Color: Gray with yellow and brown bands

Origin: Mountain ranges

Grain Size: Medium

Occurrence: Worldwide

GNEISS

Gneiss, which is often used as a building stone, is a metamorphic rock that is primarily made up of quartz, feldspar, and mica. It is classified as a high grade material—this means it has been subjected to a lot of heat and pressure. It is very widely distributed across most parts of the world, and can be composed of both igneous and sedimentary rocks, with granite being the most common. The grains within it are flattened, and are arranged in distinct bands that can separate easily—these are typically arranged in alternating layers of light minerals such as quartz and feldspar and dark ones such as biotite and hornblende. Gneiss can be easily confused with some types of schist.

Color: Variable from pale to dark

Origin: Mountain ranges

Grain Size: Coarse

Occurrence: Worldwide

KILLAS

Color: Dark gray to black

Origin: Carboniferous and Devonian strata

Grain Size: Fine

Occurrence: Worldwide

Killas is a type of rock that is composed of sedimentary sea bed material that has been metamorphosed by the enormous amount of heat that was produced when large quantities of granites were formed nearby. It occurs in both Devonian and Carboniferous strata, and is often found near, or in direct association with, valuable metal ores, such as those of copper and tin. The term "Killas" is a name that originated in the mines of south-west England. Around sixty percent of Cornwall lies over Killas, and this factor, combined with its workability, has resulted in it being widely exploited as a building stone.

SLATE

Slate is familiar to most people as a material which is used to roof houses in many parts of the world. It is a sedimentary shale-like rock that has undergone a low grade metamorphosis. During this process, it is highly compressed, and the mineral content within is flattened such that the resultant rock has very distinct cleavage planes. Slate is mostly made up of very finely divided clay minerals, with the predominant ones typically being quartz, chlorite, and muscovite, although many others, such as feldspar, apatite, kaolin, and tourmaline can also be present. Some types of slate contain relatively large amounts of pyrite.

Color: Gray to dark gray

Origin: Mountain ranges

Grain Size: Fine

Occurrence: Worldwide

SEDIMENTARY ROCKS

Sedimentary rocks are one of the three main types of rock that make up the Earth's crust. They are very common, with examples such as chalk, limestone, dolomite, sandstone, and shale being well known. Although they cover around three-quarters of the world's land area, the layer is actually comparatively thin, and they only make up about five percent of it by volume.

The majority of sedimentary rocks are of a type known as "clastic rocks"—these are formed by the erosion or decomposition of igneous and metamorphic rocks into particles. This may come about in any one of three main ways, all of which rely on the long-term accumulation of this particulate material. Regardless of which mechanism is responsible for the accumulation of the rock particles or fragments, over extended periods of time successive beds form on top of each other in a process that is referred to as superposition. Eventually, the weight imposed on those at the bottom is sufficient for them to become compacted and cemented together as rock—this is called lithification, with the various beds of rock being known as strata.

CHERT *Silicon Dioxide SiO$_2$*

Color: Variable

Hardness: 7

Cleavage: None

Fracture: Conchoidal

Crystals: Translucent to opaque

Specific Gravity: 2.55–2.65

Origin: Marine

Grain Size: Fine

Occurrence: Worldwide

Chert is a type of hard, microcrystalline quartz that is composed of chalcedony. A large amount of this rock is derived from the silicaceous skeletons of microscopic marine creatures called radiolarians. Other kinds form in non-marine environments where sedimentary rocks have been washed out and replaced by silica. Chert has a very fine grain size, and can be colored anywhere from white to gray to black. It occurs in massive layers as well as in the form of nodules in chalk or limestone. There is no clear distinction between chert, chalcedony, flint, jasper, and agate—any names that are used within this group are almost entirely subjective. This stone has a dull, pearly, or sub-vitreous luster and a colorless streak.

Silicon Dioxide SiO₂ EARLY CARBONIFEROUS CHERT

Early Carboniferous Chert is a particular kind of microcrystalline quartz that differs from other cherts in that it has a gray to black coloration, and although it is widespread, is not nearly as common. It often has layers of various impurities such as volcanic ash, clay particles, or silt—these are generally evident as brown or gray bands or stripes. They indicate that the deep sea environment in which the chert formed changed through time as differing kinds of materials were gradually deposited from the waters above. Where the lines are curved or jagged, it indicates that the material underwent some form of geological movement before the chert had fully solidified. This chert has a dull, pearly, or sub-vitreous luster and a colorless streak.

Color:	Gray to black
Hardness:	7
Cleavage:	None
Fracture:	Conchoidal
Crystals:	Translucent to opaque
Specific Gravity:	2.55–2.65
Origin:	Marine
Grain Size:	Fine
Occurrence:	Widespread

FLINT

Flint, which is a cryptocrystalline form of quartz, is composed almost entirely of silicon dioxide. This means that the crystals cannot be seen with the naked eye, but instead require the use of a high power microscope. Flint is simply a dark form of chert that under some definitions is considered to have a more waxy luster. Although it is typically almost black, it can also have various tints of red, brown, or yellow, dependent on the presence of various impurities. It varies from between being slightly translucent to opaque, and has a conchoidal fracture which can result in a razor sharp edge. This property was first exploited for the production of stone cutting tools by our early human ancestors as much as 1.5 million years ago. Since then, flint has been used for all kinds of purposes, including making sparks for lighting fires, as well as igniting the explosive charges in cannons and guns.

Color: Dark gray to black, sometimes tinted red, brown, or yellow

Origin: Marine

Grain Size: Very fine

Occurrence: Worldwide

SHALE

Color: Typically gray

Origin: Marine

Grain Size: Fine

Occurrence: Worldwide

Shale, which is the most common form of sedimentary rock, is a material that started out as mud or clay and was then compacted by the weight of rock above it. It typically results from the deposition of sediments in marine or freshwater environments where the water is still or very slow moving. They are fissile materials—this means that they split easily into thin layers. Where the rock is very dark or black, such as is common with Paleozoic and Mesozoic rocks, it is an indicator that the formation conditions were anoxic, such as those found in stagnant pools. Some shale strata contain well preserved fossils, and when good specimens are found, they can be sought after by collectors.

JURASSIC SHALE

Jurassic shales are sedimentary rocks that were laid down in quiet waters during the Jurassic era, some 145 to 200 million years ago. This was a period when dinosaurs roamed the Earth, and the seas teemed with all kinds of strange marine creatures. As a result of this, many of the shales that were laid down contain large numbers of fossils, especially those of bivalves, brachiopods, and belemnites. The specimen seen here demonstrates this well, effectively being a well preserved section of Jurassic sea bed that is composed largely of fragments of oyster-like molluscs.

Color: Typically gray

Origin: Marine

Grain Size: Fine

Occurrence: Worldwide

SANDSTONE

Color: Variable, from pale yellow to dark brown.

Origin: Marine or freshwater

Grain Size: Medium

Occurrence: Worldwide

Sandstone is a sedimentary rock that is largely made up of particles of quartz that have been bonded together with cementitious materials that are composed of such things as calcium carbonate, iron oxides, and silicaceous agents of one sort or another. There are many different varieties of sandstone, with these containing various other components such as feldspars, mica, and iron oxides like limonite. The specimen seen here is an example that was laid down during the Carboniferous era. Since sandstone has good architectural properties, it has been a popular building stone in large parts of the world for many thousands of years.

FERRUGINOUS SANDSTONE

Ferruginous Sandstone, which is also referred to as Carstone or Ginger Bread Stone, is a form of sandstone that is composed of relatively coarse particles that are held together in a poorly consolidated manner by an iron-based cement. These particles, which are mostly quartz, are usually well rounded by the action of water, indicating that they were derived from marine or freshwater environments. Ferruginous Sandstones are typically Cretaceous in origin, and are often associated with Lower Greensand deposits. They tend to be dark in color, and may well show marked purple hues. They are used as low grade building stones by the construction industry.

Color: Brown with purple hues

Origin: Marine or freshwater

Grain Size: Coarse

Occurrence: Worldwide

LIMESTONE

Color: Varies from white to brown

Origin: Marine or freshwater

Grain Size: Fine to medium

Occurrence: Worldwide

Limestone is very common, making up about a tenth of all the world's sedimentary rocks. Pure forms are almost white; however, it is usually colored by some form of impurity such as iron oxides of one sort or another. It is largely composed of calcite, with most forms being composed of the shells or skeletons of marine organisms. Typically, there is also a proportion of other minerals such as microcrystalline quartz or dolerite, as well as components of sand, clay, or silt. Some kinds of limestone, such as travertine and tufa, are derived from the evaporation of calcium-rich water.

SHELLY or FOSSILIFEROUS LIMESTONE

S helly or Fossiliferous Limestone, which is also sometimes referred to as Coquina, is a rock that is almost entirely made up of the shells of marine organisms or pieces of coral. It is usually loosely consolidated in a weak calcite cement, and is therefore not strong enough to be used for structural purposes in buildings. It can, however, be a useful source of fossil specimens, although the vast majority of such inclusions tend to be quite fragmented. Some shelly limestones were laid down in the Carboniferous era; however, the specimen seen here is of Cretaceous origin.

Color: Yellow-gray to gray

Origin: Marine or freshwater

Grain Size: Variable and Shelly

Occurrence: Worldwide

DOLOMITE *Calcium Magnesium Carbonate CaMg(CO₃)₂*

Color: White, gray, or pink

Hardness: 3.5–4

Cleavage: Perfect

Fracture: Sub-conchoidal

Crystals: Transparent on thin edges; trigonal

Specific Gravity: 2.9

Occurrence: Worldwide

Dolomite, which is also known as dolostone, is a sedimentary carbonate rock that is composed of mineralized calcium magnesium carbonate, along with various trace impurities. These are typically either iron or manganese, with the former imparting a yellow or brown hue, and the latter a pinkish color. It is named after the French geologist Déodat Gratet de Dolomieu (1750–1801), who first described it in what are now known as the Dolomitic Alps in Northern Italy, in 1791. Dolomite often replaces certain proportions of limestone, and where this has happened, the resulting material is known as dolomitic or magnesian limestone. It has a vitreous, pearly, or waxy luster and a white streak.

TRIASSIC MUDSTONE

The term Mudstone includes claystones, shales, and siltstones. These are rocks that are categorized by their particle sizes—claystones, for instance, are comprised of individual particles that are less than 4 μm in diameter. The grains in Siltstones are larger, being between 4 and 62.5 μm across. Those examples which split into thin layers are classified as shales, and ones which have both clay and silt sized particles are generally simply referred to as mudstones. The specimen seen here is a Triassic Mudstone, and so was laid down as the result of mud deposition in a still water environment somewhere between 200 and 250 million years ago.

Color: Very variable

Origin: Marine or freshwater

Grain Size: Fine

Occurrence: Worldwide

JURASSIC MUDSTONE

Jurassic Mudstone, as with the other types of mudstone, is a massive rock that is comprised of particles that are too small to be seen with the naked eye. Since it is a sedimentary material that derives from a time when the seas were full of marine organisms, some 145 to 200 million years ago, it often has fossil inclusions. The example seen here, for instance, has three ammonites (marine cephalopods related to squid and octopus, and similar to the modern day nautilus) and part of an oyster-like mollusc visible. Particularly interesting specimens of this rock are sought after by collectors.

Color: Variable, from brown to gray

Origin: Marine or freshwater

Grain Size: Fine

Occurrence: Worldwide

SILTSTONE

Color: Brown to dark gray

Origin: Marine or freshwater

Grain Size: Fine

Occurrence: Worldwide

Siltstone is a sedimentary rock that is very similar to mudstone, except that at least two thirds of the quartz grains from which it is comprised are relatively coarse. These vary between 4 and 62.5 µm in diameter, making it part way between a mudstone and a sandstone. It also has very small pore sizes, which is another good field indicator. Siltstones are typically formed in medium depth marine environments that are deeper than those where sand is formed, but shallower than the ocean floor where fine clays are deposited.

SEDIMENTARY CONCRETIONS

S edimentary rocks often end up with small voids
as the result of various components being washed
out over time. These spaces are often filled by various
mineral cements—the resulting structures are known as
concretions. In some cases these are relatively amorphous,
however, in others they are close to spherical. Typically,
they are comprised of iron sulphide in the form of pyrite,
marcasite, or pyrrhotite. The first two are non-magnetic,
whereas the latter is weakly magnetic. The specimens seen
here are of a type known as Kansas Pop Rocks—the name
alluding to the fact that they explode if thrown into a fire.

Color: Typically brown or gray

Origin: Sedimentary

Grain Size: Fine

Occurrence: Worldwide

PERMIAN BRECCIA

Color: Very variable

Origin: Sedimentary

Grain Size: Very coarse

Occurrence: Worldwide

Breccias are rocks that are composed of various pieces of rocks and minerals that have been cemented together in some form of parent matrix. They can be derived from a number of different sources, including sedimentary, igneous, impact, tectonic, and hydrothermal, and grouped by the type of materials they are made up from, their particle sizes, and so on. The specimen seen here is of a sedimentary variety which was laid down during the Permian era. Its red-brown coloration indicates that it contains a significant quantity of iron impurities. This type of material is of little interest to collectors, and as it has no mechanical strength, is of no use to the construction industry.

FAULTED BRECCIA

aulted Breccias are rocks which form as the
result of two adjacent blocks of rock that are
separated by a fault line. As these slide past each other,
the grinding action creates large quantities of small
fragments—these are later cemented together by
various minerals to create a breccia. The distance that
the particles have traveled from their source can be
determined to some extent by examination of their
shapes. Those ones which are clearly rounded have
usually been water worn, and so are likely to have
been transported some distance. Those with very
angled pieces—such as the fragments in the specimen
seen here—have not moved very far at all.

Color: Very variable

Origin: Transitional

Grain Size: Very coarse

Occurrence: Worldwide

IGNEOUS ROCKS

Igneous rocks are extremely common, but although they make up about 95 percent of the Earth's crust, they are mostly hidden by a thin layer of sedimentary and metamorphic material. There are a large number of different types—more than 700 in all, which are often found in association with important or valuable minerals. These include such examples as tin, copper, gold, silver, arsenic, uranium, tungsten, and chromium.

Igneous rocks are formed from magma—molten rock which lies beneath the surface of the Earth, typically at temperatures of 700°C to 1300°C. In this state, it is lighter than the rock from which it is formed, and so rises to the surface whenever a route develops. The rocks it forms can be either intrusive or extrusive. Intrusive rocks are those which have formed as the result of magma cooling and solidifying well below the surface. Since they are surrounded by rock, the cooling rate is very low, and as a result, generally have large crystal structures. They are therefore sufficiently coarse grained for successful examination with the naked eye.

Extrusive rocks, on the other hand, are formed when magma reaches the surface as the result of volcanic activity, and then cools, forming lavas of one kind or another.

OBSIDIAN

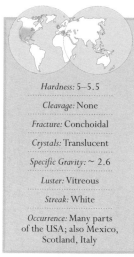

Hardness: 5–5.5

Cleavage: None

Fracture: Conchoidal

Crystals: Translucent

Specific Gravity: ~ 2.6

Luster: Vitreous

Streak: White

Occurrence: Many parts of the USA; also Mexico, Scotland, Italy

Obsidian, which is a form of volcanic glass that has an amorphous structure, is formed by molten lava being quenched by coming into contact with a body of water, such as the ocean or a lake. It is colored by the presence of iron and magnesium, and can occur both in massive forms and as small nodules. Sometimes it can have interesting optical effects caused by the inclusion of small bubbles of trapped air—these varieties are referred to as Rainbow or Sheen Obsidian. A further variant has large numbers of white crystals of cristobalite distributed throughout its structure—this form is known as Snowflake Obsidian. When fractured, obsidian has razor sharp edges—this property has been exploited since the earliest times for the manufacture of stone tools.

PUMICE

Pumice is a lightweight rock that is formed during volcanic eruptions when molten pyroclastic material is thrown high into the air. As this cools and sets, it traps pockets of air throughout its structure—as a result of this, it is typically about 90 percent porous; many varieties are light enough to float in water. It is usually very pale in color, ranging from white to gray; however, the specimen seen here has been colored brown by iron oxide contamination. Pumice has been used to make lightweight concrete since Roman times, and it is also incorporated into many cosmetic products as well as industrial scouring powders.

Color: Variable from light to dark

Origin: Extrusive

Grain Size: Fine

Occurrence: Worldwide

VESICULAR BASALT

Color: Typically dark brown to black with purplish hues

Origin: Extrusive

Grain Size: Fine

Occurrence: Worldwide

Basalt is a common extrusive volcanic rock with a fine grain size that can be found worldwide. It is formed when lava is cooled rapidly on exposure to air. The specimen seen here is of a variety that is full of small to medium sized holes known as vesicles—consequently it is referred to as vesicular basalt. Most forms are dark brown to black, and usually have a purplish hue. The proportion of mineral content varies significantly, with the main constituents being feldspar, olivine, plagioclase, pyroxene, and silica, along with various compounds of iron, sodium, calcium, magnesium, and aluminum.

DOLERITE

D olerite, which is also known as diabase, is a widely distributed and extremely common igneous rock. It is a coarse grained, intrusive form of basalt, and there are several different kinds, including quartzdolerite, mica-dolerite, porphyritic-dolerite, and olivine-dolerite. They occur as dykes and sills, and all are primarily composed of the typical basaltic minerals, along with others such as biotite, hornblende, and apatite. Dolerite is not a particularly attractive material, and so is only used for low-grade construction applications like road building. With a specific gravity of around 3.0, it is a relatively dense rock.

Color: Red-brown to black

Origin: Intrusive

Grain Size: Medium

Occurrence: Worldwide as dykes and sills

WHITE GRANITE

Color: Light

Origin: Intrusive

Grain Size: Coarse

Occurrence: Worldwide

Granite is an intrusive igneous rock that is formed from magma and composed of crystalline granules of various minerals. The size, color, and make up of these varies between types, with orthoclase feldspar, plagioclase feldspar, tourmaline, quartz, mica, biotite, and hornblende being the main constituents. The example seen here is of a type known as white granite—others can be pink, gray, or nearly black. It is a hard wearing material that occurs as massive layers, and can form large outcrops known as tors or massifs. It is an excellent building material, and has been used since prehistoric times for construction and ornamental purposes.

FELDSPATHIC GRANITE

Feldspathic granite is a type that has a greater than usual feldspar content, as can be seen in the specimen here. It is a coarsely crystalline example from the Isles of Scilly, south-west England—a location that forms part of an extensive geological area called the "Cornubian Orefield." This formed between 270 and 300 million years ago, as the result of rocks being melted deep in the Earth's crust. As the zone cooled and crystallized, many minerals were also deposited, creating a valuable source of ores for things like copper, tin, silver, gold, and arsenic.

Color:	Light
Origin:	Intrusive
Grain Size:	Coarse
Occurrence:	Worldwide

GABBRO

Color: Typically dark green to black

Origin: Intrusive

Grain Size: Coarse

Occurrence: Worldwide

Gabbro is an intrusive igneous rock that makes up large parts of the Earth's crust, especially in deep oceanic areas. It is derived from molten magma that has cooled and crystallized before reaching the Earth's surface, and occurs as massive forms. Gabbro has a similar composition to that of basalt, being primarily made up of plagioclase feldspar, olivine, and pyroxene. There are usually also small amounts of other minerals present, such as magnetite and ilmenite. It has a coarse grain structure, with the crystals typically being more than 1 mm in diameter. It is typically dark green to black, and can often contain valuable minerals, such as gold, silver, chromium, copper, cobalt, and nickel.

RHYOLITE

Rhyolite is a fine-grained extrusive volcanic rock that contains quartz, biotite, mica, hornblende, pyroxene, and both alkali and plagioclase feldspar. It is closely related to granite, with the main difference being that its crystal structure cannot be seen with the naked eye. It is formed when molten lavas are ejected high into the air by explosive volcanic eruptions, as well as when lava flows cool down. The density of the resulting rock varies depending on the manner of formation. Rhyolite is generally a gray to purple color, sometimes red-brown or black, and is used for a variety of construction purposes in many different parts of the world.

Color: Very variable, from light to red-brown, to gray, or black

Origin: Extrusive

Grain Size: Fine

Occurrence: Worldwide

TEKTITE *(SiO)(AlO)(FeO)Mg, Na, KO*

Color: Black, green, or colorless

Hardness: 6–7

Cleavage: Absent

Fracture: Conchoidal

Crystals: Variable

Specific Gravity: ~2.5

Occurrence: E. Europe (Moldavia region), SE Asia (Thailand), Australia, & USA (Georgia)

Tektites are vitreous materials that are found in association with meteorite impact craters. Their exact origins are not fully understood, but the most widely accepted hypothesis is that they are a kind of glass that is formed by the extreme heat and pressure generated when a meteorite hits the Earth. They vary in size from microscopic to pieces that weigh several pounds, and are structurally amorphous, being mostly composed of silica glass. They also contain trace impurities of various elements including magnesium, sodium, aluminum, potassium, and iron—the relative quantities of these being responsible for the final coloration. Most examples are opaque, but they can be anywhere from transparent to translucent.

Silica and Various Metallic Oxides MOLDAVITE

The term Moldavite was originally given to a type of tektite that was found in the Moldau Valley in the Czech Republic. These days, however, any tektite that has a similar form tends to be labeled with the same appellation. It is typically a bottle green color; however, it can also be colorless or even black. It occurs as distinct fragments that lack any clearly defined shape or crystal structure, and while it bears many resemblances to obsidian, its actual origins remain unexplained. Moldavites are highly sought after by both jewelers and specimen collectors—exceptional examples are set as valuable gemstones. This stone has a vitreous to dull luster and a white streak.

Hardness: 5–6

Cleavage: None

Fracture: Conchoidal

Crystals: Variable; most are opaque, but also transparent to translucent; amorphous

Specific Gravity: 2.5

Occurrence: Moldavia region of E. Europe, Thailand and SE Asia, Australia, and USA

GLOSSARY

Alluvial deposit
Particles of sediment or other material deposited by a running body of water.

Breccia A sedimentary rock made up of medium-sized angular fragments that have been bonded together with a natural cement.

Carboniferous The geological time period that stretches from around 365–290 million years ago.

Clast A small fragment of rock that has been broken or eroded off a larger piece.

Cleavage
A characteristic property of some rocks and minerals to split apart along distinct parallel planes.

Conglomerate
A sedimentary rock made up of pieces of rocks that have been worn into rounded shapes and then bonded together with a natural cement.

Cretaceous The geological time period that stretches from around 145–65 million years ago.

Devonian The geological time period that stretches from around 415–360 million years ago.

Dyke An intrusion of igneous rock that is typically vertical or steeply inclined.

Foliation A rock structure that is composed of small platy minerals such as clays and micas.

Fossil The remains of an animal or plant that has been preserved in rock.

Gneiss A common high-grade metamorphic rock formed from igneous or sedimentary materials.

Igneous A type of rock that is formed by the cooling of intrusive or extrusive magma.

Intrusion A formation of igneous rock that has forced its way into pre-existing rocks.

Jurassic The geological time period that stretches from around 200–145 million years ago.

Lava Molten material which is expelled by a volcanic eruption.

Magma Molten material that forms igneous rocks when it cools.

Massive A bulk form of a rock or mineral.

Matrix The fine material which fills the voids in a coarse-grained cemented structure.

Mica A complex series of shiny minerals with a flexible, platy structure and perfect cleavage.

Mudstone A sedimentary rock that is composed of fine-grained particles.

Pegmatite A very coarse-grained igneous rock.

Permian The geological time period that stretches from around 300–250 million years ago.

Pyroclastic Pieces of material that have been thrown up as the result of violent volcanic activity.

Sandstone A sedimentary rock that is mostly composed of sand-sized quartz grains.

Schist A medium-grade metamorphic rock that is mostly composed of elongated minerals.

Sediment A particulate material that has settled out of suspension in still water.

Sedimentary rocks Rocks that are composed of sediments that have been compacted and lithified.

Shale A soft, fine-grained, many layered, sedimentary rock composed of compacted sediments.

Sill An intrusion of igneous rock similar to a dyke but in a roughly horizontal orientation.

Silt A fine sediment that has a particle size between those of sand and mud.

Siltstone A fine-grained sedimentary rock that is composed of particles with sizes between those of sand and mud.

Slate An easily split metamorphic rock with a fine grain that is formed from shale or mudstone.

Tuff A rock that is mostly composed of volcanic ash.

Vein A crack in a rock that has been filled with a solid material composed of crystal and/or minerals.

INDEX

PICTURE CREDITS

The majority of photographs in this book were taken by the author,
James Lagomarsino. He would especially like to thank the staff
at the Exeter headquarters of "Crystals" (www.crystalshop.co.uk),
who provided access to the majority of the specimens shown
in this book from their fabulous stock of minerals.

The author would also like to thank the staff at the Museum of
Barnstaple and North Devon for their kind assistance in providing
access to their excellent mineral collection, as well as to Mike Burns,
Dave Cottey, and Teresa Price for their contributions.

© Digital Vision: pages 11, 13, 14, 21, 31, 35

© Impala/Fotolia: pages 20, 61

© Ingrid Walter/Fotolia: page 68

© Jerzy Czarkowski/Fotolia: page 76